Getting Started in Amateur Radio

by

Steve Nichols, G0KYA

Radio Society of Great Britain

Published by the Radio Society of Great Britain, 3 Abbey Court, Priory Business Park, Bedford MK44 3WH.

Web site: www.rsgb.org

Tel: 01234 832700

ISBN: 9871 9101 9311 2

First Published 2015

Reprinted 2017 & 2018

Digitally Reprinted 2020 onwards

Design & Editing: Steve White, G3ZVW

Cover Design: Kevin Williams, M6ACB

Production: Mark Allgar, M1MPA

Printed in Great Britain by 4Edge Ltd of Hockley, Essex

Publisher's note
The opinions expressed in this book are those of the author(s) and are not necessarily those of the Radio Society of Great Britain. Whilst the information presented is believed to be correct, the publishers and their agents cannot accept responsibility for consequences arising from any inaccuracies or omissions.

Any amendments or updates to this book can be found at: www.rsgb.org/booksextra

Contents

Chapter 1   Introduction   1

Chapter 2   Getting your Foundation licence   5

Chapter 3   Your first VHF/UHF radio   11

Chapter 4   Your first HF radio   17

Chapter 5   Other equipment you might need   28

Chapter 6   Practical antennas   31

Chapter 7   Basic FM and SSB operating   44

Chapter 8   CW and digital modes   49

Chapter 9   A propagation primer   59

Chapter 10   DXing, Contesting, QSLing and Awards   70

Chapter 11   What else is there?   82

Preface

Amateur radio is an amazing hobby that has so many different facets there is always something for everyone.

In fact, if you took the time to get fully involved in VHF DXing, microwaves, Moonbounce, HF DXing, digital modes, low power, contesting, Summits on the Air, special events and all the other elements of the hobby, you wouldn't have time for anything else in your life.

What about receiving digital images from the International Space Station? Or talking to friends around the world via a real-life satellite? Both of these things are possible with amateur radio.

And the good news is that it has never been easier to get an amateur radio licence. Years ago you would probably have had to attend a six-month long theory course and undertake a 12 words per minute Morse code exam, but now you can get your Foundation Licence in a couple of weekends, just sitting a straightforward multiple choice paper.

The Foundation Licence gives you access to nearly all the bands available, with a maximum power of 10 watts output. Think that doesn't sound like much? Would you believe you can work the world with 10 watts? You betcha, as thousands of radio amateurs have proved.

As you progress through the hobby you can take your Intermediate and Advanced licences, which help build your knowledge and give you access to more power and more opportunities, such as being able to use your radio on holidays overseas.

This book is aimed at those who are considering getting into the hobby, or have just obtained their first licence. It goes though some of the fundamentals of what you can do and how you can set up your own amateur radio station. It also looks at buying a radio, the basics of antennas, propagation, digital modes and much more.

I hope you enjoy reading it.

Steve Nichols, G0KYA
February 2015

Dedication

To my wife Toni, who continues to put up with
my obsession with amateur radio.

Chapter 1.
Introduction

What is amateur radio?

Amateur radio is a fantastic hobby that attracts devotees from all parts of the globe. The fact you are reading this book either means you want to find out more about the hobby or you have already taken your first steps to gain an amateur radio Foundation licence.

So what is amateur radio? A dictionary definition might describe it as 'A popular technical pastime and public service that uses designated radio frequencies for the non-commercial exchange of messages, wireless experimentation, self-training, and emergency communications'. Note that it is non commercial – radio amateurs, or radio hams as they are sometimes called, engage in the hobby for the sheer pleasure they get from it. In fact, the word 'amateur' comes from the Latin word 'amor', meaning love.

How did it all start?

Amateur radio has been with us since the very birth of radio. You could argue that Guglielmo Marconi was the first radio amateur when he received signals in Newfoundland from his transmitter in Poldhu, Cornwall in 1901.

In fact it was interest in early experiments like these that prompted the first true radio amateurs to try and replicate the early pioneers' success.

For example, MJC Dennis set up what is thought to be the first amateur

The Marconi memorial at Poldhu, Cornwall.

radio station at Woolwich Arsenal in 1898. Others followed suit and in 1904 the UK Wireless Telegraphy Act became law, laying down the foundation that people were required to obtain a licence before they could transmit. In those days there was no commercial equipment so amateurs had to build their own transmitters and receivers.

Getting Started in Amateur Radio

A 1910 announcement by the then HM Postmaster General licensed "experimental wireless", which gave radio amateurs the ability to innovate without commercial or statutory controls. Unfortunately the outbreak of World War One resulted in all licences being revoked and equipment being impounded. After the war experimentation started again, although amateurs were relegated to the 'short wave' bands, which were thought to be useless for anything other than very short distance communication.

This turned out to be a major coup, as it soon became apparent that amateurs were able to make very long distance contacts on these bands indeed. Soon the challenge was on to bridge the Atlantic, a hurdle that was soon beaten.

Soon after, contacts were being made from the UK to New Zealand. Technology developed in the 1920s and 30s, with amateurs often at the forefront of proving just how useful radio waves could be.

The Second World War once again put a temporary stop to amateur activity, but the post-war period and 1950s were the heydays for amateur radio, as new techniques and equipment were developed.

The 1960s and 70s brought commercially-available equipment to the radio ham, much of it starting to originate in the Far East, as Japan entered the market.

The last 40-odd years have seen radios getting smaller, yet more capable, and as you will see later computing technology has now joined with amateur radio to create a powerful union.

The present day

The amateur radio service is carefully regulated by the International Telecommunication Union (ITU). Radio amateurs have to pass examinations before they are allowed on the air and are issued with a licence for their operations.

Amateurs use a variety of modes to make contacts.

Radio amateurs today use a variety of voice, text, image, and data communication modes and have access to frequency allocations throughout the RF spectrum to enable communication from as little as a few metres to across the world.

They may just be "amateurs", but that hasn't stopped them developing new radio techniques to enhance communications across the airwaves.

One of the most famous amateurs is Joe Taylor (callsign K1JT). Joe developed a new mode called WSJT, which is used for very weak signal communication. In his day job Joe is an American astrophysicist and won a Nobel Prize for his discovery with Russell Alan Hulse of a new type of pulsar.

Other leading engineers and technologists are also radio amateurs, such as Professor Sir Martin Sweeting G3YJO, the executive chairman of Guildford-based SSTL, Britain's leading satellite company.

What can you do with amateur radio?

To explain everything you can do with the hobby would take a book in itself, but let's look at some of the highlights. With amateur radio you can:

- Contact people all over the world, which often leads to developing international friendships
- Compete in international competitions to test how effective your equipment is and how good you are as an operator
- Chase awards for contacting other like-minded individuals all over the world
- Perform technical experiments — many of the leaps forward in radio technology have been initiated by radio amateurs
- Communicate through amateur space satellites or with the International Space Station (which carries an amateur radio station)
- Provide communications at times of national and weather-related emergencies.

But please don't think you need to have a PhD in electronics to become a radio amateur. While many people are keen to design and build their own equipment, others prefer just to chat with other like-minded individuals and don't want to push the boundaries when it comes to technical design. That's not a problem. You don't have a to be a technical guru to take your first steps and get a Foundation licence, although it can get a little more technical once you move on to the Intermediate and Advanced licences.

Whatever your interest in radio communications, you will find others sharing it — from 'geeky' experimenters to those just interested in communicating by radio.

Local radio clubs can help you gain your licence and develop your skills. While other activities may appeal to both you and your family.

Activities like direction finding (similar to orienteering, but with a high-tech "spin"), field days out in the open, and Summits on the Air, when amateurs operate from hill and mountain tops, can all be "family friendly" too.

A slow-scan TV image received by amateurs and sent from the International Space Station.

Or what about helping to run a special event station at a local museum or tourist attraction – there are special event days in the calendar for everything from railways to windmills.

The public generally associate amateur radio with the short wave bands, with amateurs being capable of talking to others across the world given the right conditions.

It is true that HF operations still feature highly, but that is only part of the story.

Others are keen to push the boundaries of microwave or satellite operations, seeing just how far they can work from portable stations on hilltops or perfecting their station so that they can talk to other like-minded enthusiasts on the other side of the Atlantic via a fast-moving low earth orbiting satellite.

Or if that doesn't float your boat, how about low power (QRP) operations where

Getting Started in Amateur Radio

This tiny low power (QRP) transceiver is quite capable of making contacts worldwide.

people try to make contact with just a couple of watts from home-made transceivers? Not only do they succeed, but the distances they manage put many high power operators to shame.

Others have shown that they can actually bounce their signals off the surface of the moon, contacting other amateurs across the globe with a characteristic signal delay of about two and a half seconds.

The hobby also lends itself to the application of computer technology. Most hams have a computer in their "shack" and these are often connected up to the radio to allow digital communications between individuals.

Modes like radio teletype (RTTY) and PSK31 (which allows worldwide contacts with only a few watts and simple antennas) are very popular. Many thought that computers would make amateur radio redundant, but the hobby has had a resurgence of interest thanks to the humble PC.

It is now possible to key in the callsign of the person you are talking to, and find a map of where they are with lots of other details, such as their hobbies and interests. The same computer can be used to log the contact details, which can then be uploaded to a server to help you win awards.

Radio repeaters can even be linked to the internet so that person with a handheld radio on top of a mountain can have a perfectly clear conversation with someone else on another summit as far away as New Zealand.

The future

Amateur radio has a bright future. It is the ideal training ground for young people who want a career in electronics or radio communications. Plus amateurs are pushing forward the boundaries of what can be done with digital communications every day. In the future there will be many more exciting technological developments, in areas we can only dream of.

Older people are also discovering that amateur radio can be a fantastic hobby in later life, enabling them to indulge in a passion that they may have held since they were teenagers, but didn't have the time or money to pursue back then. It lets them have friends, even if they are housebound or miles away from the nearest community.

You can get a radio licence in as little as a couple of weekends, with radio equipment prices starting at lower levels now than ever before.

Many young people find amateur radio is a great training ground for a career in electronics.

If this has inspired you to find out more, read on. We'll look at what you need to do to get an amateur radio licence and what you can do with it once you have one.

The world really will be your oyster.

Chapter 2. Getting your Foundation licence

Getting an amateur radio licence is a lot easier than you might think.

In years gone by you would have to study for up to six months and take a Morse Code test before being let loose on the HF bands to make worldwide contacts, but now you can study for and pass your Foundation licence test in as little as a weekend.

The Foundation licence is your gateway to amateur radio. The course and exam that leads to the licence provides you with an exciting introduction to the hobby, while requiring an acceptable minimum level of skill and experience.

The licence is recognised by the UK communications regulator Ofcom and entitles you to take a unique identifier, called a callsign, which will be used to identify you when you are transmitting.

The Foundation courses usually take place locally, in a friendly and informal environment and are conducted by experienced radio amateurs, often at a local radio club.

The RSGB website at www.rsgb.org has a page that will help you locate your nearest club, simply by using your location or postcode.

Most of the training is practical. There is a small amount of radio and electronics theory, but only enough for you to appreciate things like using the correct fuses in your equipment and how to build an antenna to get the most out of your radio station.

Your course will take 10 to 12 hours to complete and can be spread out over a few weeks or weekends.

Don't be put off by the thought of having to do an exam. The Foundation licence exam is very straightforward and consists of 26 multiple choice questions, which you have

The RSGB's book *Foundation Licence NOW!* tells you everything you need to know to pass your exam.

55 minutes to answer. For the Foundation licence exam there is a fee, currently £27.50. Your exam paper is checked by the invigilator straight after the exam, before the formal marking is carried out electronically at the RSGB Examinations Department.

Getting Started in Amateur Radio

Once marked you will then receive an official result sheet in the post from the RSGB Examinations Department. This takes at least six working days from the receipt of your exam paper. If you have passed, you will at the same time receive a certificate and your candidate number. The examination office will upload your pass to the UK communications regulator Ofcom, who are responsible for issuing amateur radio licences. You may then log on to the Ofcom licensing system to apply for your licence. Make sure you have your candidate number to hand, because you will need this to complete the process.

If you apply for your Foundation licence on the Ofcom website, your licence is free of charge.

You will either be allocated a callsign, such as M6ABC, or you can choose your own callsign suffix if it is available.

The prefix M6 identifies you as a Foundation licence holder operating in England. Other prefixes are allocated according to your home location, such as MM for Scotland, MW for Wales, MI for Northern Ireland, MD for the Isle of Man, MJ for Jersey and MU for Guernsey.

If you operate in one of these regions of the UK you have to temporarily change your prefix. So M6ABC would become MM6ABC if you were operating in Scotland on holiday, for example.

As you will learn on your Foundation course, it gets a little more complicated. If operating portable it is recommended you add /P to the end of your callsign, so if M6ABC is operating portable while on holiday in Scotland he or she would sign MM6ABC/P. The other designators include /M if mobile and /A if at an alternative address. Don't worry, it will all become clear when you do your Foundation course.

Once you have your Foundation licence you are ready to make your first transmission on the amateur radio bands – an exciting moment!

You are then free to operate on the most frequently used amateur bands, without supervision,

RadCom, the RSGB member magazine, has regular features for newcomers to the hobby.

up to a power of 10 watts. This might not sound like very much power, but once you have acquired experience operating your radio you will find it is enough to communicate almost anywhere in the world.

To find out more call the RSGB Examinations Department on 01234 832 700 or see the RSGB website at www.rsgb.org

The Foundation licence gives you access to a lot of the amateur bands and with 10W you can have plenty of fun – especially if you make sure you use efficient antennas.

But there is life beyond the Foundation licence, so let's take a look at what you can move on to next.

Moving up - Intermediate and Advanced licences

The next step is the Intermediate licence. There is no compulsion to upgrade your licence to the next level, but if you do you will gain more knowledge and skills. You will also enjoy additional privileges, including higher power limits, more frequencies, and you will be permitted to build your own transmitting equipment.

The main advantage of stepping up to the Intermediate licence is the increase in permitted operating power. You will be able to go from the 10 Watts of the Foundation licence up to 50 Watts.

The best way to undergo the training for the Intermediate licence is with a recognised course, perhaps at your local club.

If you decide to go for the Intermediate licence you will need to complete two assessments. The first is a practical skills assessment that demonstrates your competence in basic electronics. This involves soldering a rudimentary circuit together, using some of the components you will learn about on the course. This is followed by an examination of 45 multiple-choice questions, each with four possible responses, which covers the remainder of the syllabus. The examination lasts one hour and 25 minutes.

Andy Goldsmith, M0NKR progressed through the Foundation and Intermediate licences before obtaining his Advanced amateur radio licence.

For the Intermediate licence course exam there is a fee (£32.50 at the time of writing) payable to the RSGB, plus there may be other fees payable to a local club if you use their facilities. Your exam paper will be sent to RSGB and marked electronically. Final confirmation of your result will come from the society.

Once a pass is confirmed you will receive a certificate from the RSGB Examinations Department. This should be around six days after receipt of your exam paper. The Examinations Department will upload your pass to the UK communications regulator Ofcom, who are responsible for issuing amateur radio licences. You may then log on to the Ofcom licensing system to apply for your licence.

You will be allocated a 2E licence, such as 2E0ABC. Similar rules apply if you are not in England. For example, it might be 2M0ABC if you are in Scotland, or 2W0ABC if you are in Wales. If operating in another part of the UK, such as when you are on holiday, the same rules as the Foundation licence apply regarding changing the prefix and also adding a suffix, such as /P if portable.

Once you have your Intermediate licence you can think about studying for your Advanced licence. This gives you a lot of additional privileges, not least of which is that you will be able to transmit up to 400 watts of power.

Getting Started in Amateur Radio

The other privileges include:

- The ability to legally transmit from almost every country in the world (countries that have implemented CEPT Recommendation T/R 61-01).
- The ability to operate maritime mobile.
- The ability to obtain notices of variation, such as the ability to access the extra 2m spectrum from 146.000-147.000 Megahertz, 600m (472-479kHz) and 60m (5MHz).
- The ability to apply for special event callsigns and supervise their operation.
- You can also supervise the assessment of Foundation and Intermediate licence holders' practicals (subject to the overall supervision of a Registered Assessor).
- You can become a GB2RS newsreader.
- You can supervise the use of greetings messages by non-licensed persons.

Operating a special event station, such as for International Marconi Day (pictured), can be great fun.

There is no practical assessment for the Advanced examination, so it is possible to study at home on your own or by distance learning, as well as at a local amateur radio club. The Advanced exam consists of a written examination paper of 62 multiple choice questions, each with four possible responses. The examination lasts two hours and it is available seven times a year.

For the Advanced Radio Communications Exam there is a fee of £37.50, payable to the RSGB. There may be other fees payable to a local club, if you use their facilities. The exam papers are sent to RSGB headquarters for electronic marking. If you pass, your certificate will be issued about six days after receipt of your papers, and Ofcom notified at the same time. You then follow the same procedure as the Intermediate licence, but your allocated callsign will be in the (current) range in the form M0ABC, with the usual rules regarding regional prefixes applying.

Operating overseas

You may be wondering about whether you can operate in other countries, in which case you may be surprised to find that it can be easier than you think – as long as you have an Advanced UK licence.

If you have a Foundation or Intermediate licence then the general rule is that you will *not* be able to operate, although there are a few exceptions (e.g Australia). Either way you are advised to check with the national amateur radio society of that country. The International Amateur Radio Union (IARU) web site maintains a list at www.iaru.org/iaru-soc.html

Many countries now subscribe to CEPT (European Conference of Postal and Telecommunication Administrations) licensing. CEPT is a group with almost 50 European and other countries. CEPT has agreed a common standard of amateur radio licence (T/R 61-01) that lets amateurs operate in another member's country. Only temporary operation is permitted under CEPT rules, for example from hotel accommodation, visiting foreign amateurs, or when mobile or portable.

An Advanced licence will let you operate overseas, like these hams on a DXpedition to Rodriquez Island in the Indian Ocean.

If the country is a CEPT signatory (and the visit is for less than three months) then assuming you have a Full/Advanced licence, to operate under CEPT regulations you need to have with you your UK licence validation document, a copy of the UK licensing regulations (Section 2 of your licence) and a copy of the foreign country's licensing regulations.

You will need to contact the foreign country's licensing administration to obtain a copy of the latter. Details can be obtained via their national society.

When operating abroad you add the regional prefix to your own callsign. For example, M0ABC would become F/M0ABC if operating in France. In fact, if you were operating portable in France you would sign as F/M0ABC/P. If you want to operate long-term (more than three months) you need to apply for a reciprocal licence. But for short-term holiday use operating under a CEPT agreement is fine.

When operating anywhere overseas you need to comply with the regulations of the foreign country you are visiting. It is your responsibility to find out the frequencies, modes and powers that you may use.

If you are intending to operate from a hotel or rented holiday accommodation it is good practice to obtain permission from the owner first. There have been isolated cases of local law enforcement authorities being unaware of the licensing regulations and it is always better to ask first!

In the unlikely event of you having difficulties with your licence when operating abroad, contact Ofcom or the RSGB.

For more information, see your UK licence or ERO Document Recommendation TR61-01 – just Google 'TR61-01' for the latest edition.

This document gives you a list of the countries in which you can work. Despite this being a European directive a number of non-European countries have also signed up to TR61-01. These include Australia, Israel, New Zealand, South Africa and the USA.

Will a full licence you might even be allowed to operate special stations overseas – this is the author at W6RO on the Queen Mary in Long Beach, California.

Getting Started in Amateur Radio

If you are travelling to a non-CEPT country then things get a little more complex. In this case you would need to apply for a reciprocal licence.

But again, reciprocal agreements **do not apply to Foundation or Intermediate licensees**.

At the moment not all countries have followed the UK by abandoning the Morse test requirement for an HF licence. If you do not hold a full UK old-style Class-A Full licence, you would be well advised to check that you will be able to operate on HF in any country you are travelling to.

Assuming you do have the appropriate UK licence, the callsign you will be issued is sometimes your own callsign with the foreign country's suffix or prefix or a callsign allocated in their normal series.

The usual way to apply for a reciprocal licence is to apply before you leave for your holiday, leaving plenty of time.

Due to overseas post and administration delays, it is generally best to allow at least two to three months for your application to be processed – longer if it is a developing country where amateur radio is not so sympathetically regarded!

If you want to know more a good starting point is the national radio amateur's society that looks after the well being of that country's amateurs. A list may be found at http://www.iaru.org/iaru-soc.html.

The RSGB publishes an excellent book – The World Licensing and Operating Directory – that has a wealth of advice to help you operate abroad with confidence, and is highly recommended.

There is also a very useful page on operating overseas on the RSGB web site at www.rsgb.org

Chapter 3.
Your first VHF/UHF radio

When you are first licensed, the first thing you probably want to do is buy a radio. But what type? And for what bands?

To generalise, VHF (2m or 144MHz) and UHF (70cms or 430MHz) are used for short distance contacts, perhaps up to 25-50 miles, whereas MF/HF (1.8-30MHz) is used for longer distances, perhaps around Europe or across the world.

That isn't to say that you can't use VHF or UHF for longer distances, because it is quite possible to work hundreds of miles via tropospheric propagation or thousands of miles with satellite communication or moonbounce.

You can also use 3.5MHz and 7MHz to work stations quite close to you via something called Near Vertical Incidence Skywave (NVIS) propagation, but if you want to talk to a friend a few miles away 2m or 70cms would be a better bet.

Many areas have local 'nets' (regular conversations) on 2m that you can join in with, plus the GB2RS news service is broadcast on 2m as well in some areas. You'll need to check what is available in your locality.

If you want to talk directly to someone in the USA, then using 20m (14MHz) is probably going to be a lot easier than building a VHF/UHF moon bounce station – at least for a beginner!

For many new hams their first radio is a handheld VHF/UHF transceiver.

So, having separated the two, let's see what you could buy for VHF/UHF. The first question you need to ask yourself is do you want a handheld, a mobile or a base station?

2m/70cm handheld

A typical 2m/70cms handheld will let you have simplex QSOs (conversations) within perhaps a 5-10 mile radius. But use your local repeater and this gets boosted up to more than 20 miles, depending on where the repeater is relative to you, plus your local terrain.

Getting Started in Amateur Radio

A repeater is simply a booster that takes your signal, amplifies it and retransmits it on a slightly different frequency, usually from an antenna mounted high up and in the clear. There are lots of 2m and 70cm repeaters around the UK that make VHF and UHF operations much easier for low power, portable and mobile stations. See www.ukrepeater.net for a list.

The upside of a VHF or UHF handy (as we call them) is that they are very portable. The downside is that without an external antenna your range may be a little limited. Also, battery life can be quite short – you may need to charge it every day or have more than one battery. Nevertheless, hand portables are good value for money and can offer a lot of enjoyment.

Many also offer dual-band capability, including the UHF 70cm (430MHz) band. For just a little more money you can then get access to two bands. Ranges on 70cm can be slightly less than 2m, but there are a lot of 70cm repeaters around the UK.

If you had to choose between a single band 2m or 70cm handheld I would recommend you go for the 2m one. There is nothing wrong with 70cm, but there is likely to be more activity on 2m.

It is best to ask a local radio amateur if they would recommend you buy a 70cm transceiver – they will know if there is much activity in your area.

Obviously, if you buy a dual-band handheld, you get the best of both worlds.

2m/70cm base stations

You can also buy dedicated 2m/70cm base station transceivers. These are bigger, bulkier and more costly than a mobile unit, but often have the power supply built in. If you are serious about operating on the VHF/UHF bands, perhaps on SSB as well, they can be a good investment, although

Some modern radios combine HF, VHF and UHF, all in one box.

you should expect to pay a lot more for one than you would for a mobile.

2m/70cm mobile transceivers

These are designed to work in your vehicle and run off the 12V supply. Generally, they have a higher power output than a handheld (often up to 60 or so Watts, compared with a typical handheld's 5W), although the power can usually be reduced if need be.

If using it in the car, the radio needs to be mounted securely

Mobile transceivers are designed to operate on 12 volts.

and carefully wired in, perhaps straight to the vehicle's battery. You can use a mobile transceiver at home too, but you will need a dedicated 12V power supply, capable of supplying enough current, plus an external antenna.

If you are likely to want to use your radio in your car and at home on a regular basis, a mobile transceiver and a 12V power supply is likely to be a better option than a handheld.

Getting the most out of your 2m/70cm radio

Most 2m and 70cm transceivers are quite complex devices and if using them on repeaters you have to think about the transmit frequency shift and selecting the correct CTCSS (Continuous Tone-Coded Squelch System) code – but more on that later. An easy way around this is to program your local repeaters into memory. That way, all you have to do is dial up the channel you want and start talking.

Some radios will automatically apply the repeater shift, while others have to have it programmed in. You will need to read the instruction manual to find out how your radio works. If you are using 2m repeaters you need to program in a -600kHz shift. That is, when you transmit, the radio will transmit 600kHz lower than the receive frequency. So, for example, if you were listening to your local repeater on 145.600MHz, you would program your radio to transmit on 145.000MHz. If you are using 70cm, you generally need to transmit 1.6MHz higher than the frequency you are listening on. So, if listening to a repeater on 433.150MHz, you will have to transmit on 434.750MHz.

Another point to consider with 2m (145 MHz) is that a lot of the repeater channels are at 12.5 kHz spacing. For example, GB3EA in East Anglia is on 145.6875 MHz. If you leave your radio on 25kHz channel spacing when scanning you may be missing out on a lot of repeaters!

We call this 'duplex' operation. If you are just talking to someone without using a repeater, i.e. transmitting and receiving on the same frequency, we call that 'simplex' operation.

If using a repeater with duplex operation we now have to program in the correct CTCSS code. CTCSS is a sub-audible tone that is imposed on your transmitted audio. Repeaters are configured to only activate if the tone you are transmitting matches the tone it is configured for. This minimises the risk of you opening another repeater on the same frequency, which is something that can occur when we get tropospheric enhancements, or 'lifts', when repeaters a hundred or more miles away can be heard on the same frequency as your local one.

Many radios will let you allocate an alphanumeric name to a memory channel, such as the repeater shown here.

An example of this is that in Norfolk the GB3NB repeater operates on 145.625MHz and uses a CTCSS tone of 94.8Hz. In Kent the GB3KS repeater operates on the same frequency, but uses a CTCSS tone of 103.5Hz. In the summer GB3KS is often heard in Norfolk, but the different CTCSS tones mean that users of each repeater are unlikely to activate the wrong one.

Just find the correct CTCSS code for your local repeater – see www.ukrepeater.net – and add it when programming the memory channels. Make sure to test it afterwards

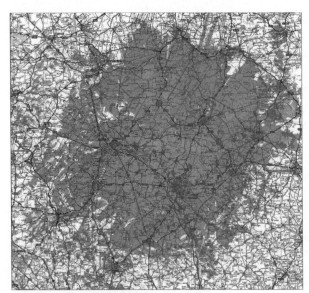

**There are repeaters all over the UK.
This is the coverage map for
the 70cm repeater GB3PY in Cambridge.**

though. Some transceivers even let you add an alpha-numeric name tag to the memory as well, which makes identification easier. You can then add a few other repeaters too, especially in regions you visit regularly.

And while you are at it, why not program all the local chat frequencies you use, such as 145.500MHz (the 2m calling channel), 145.525MHz (used for GB2RS news broadcasts), 145.250MHz (used for slow Morse transmissions) and 145.550MHz (used for rally/exhibition talk-in)? There might well be others you want to include as well.

It might also be worth considering an alternative antenna. Most handhelds have a small, compromise, flexible or 'rubber duck' antenna that works, but isn't the best. Something longer might allow you to access repeaters a bit further away, when you are out portable.

No handheld will work without a charged battery, so it makes sense to ensure yours is always charged. It might pay to keep a spare battery too, but make sure you protect the terminals from short circuiting.

And if you find that your handheld is always flat when you come to use it consider storing it with the battery off. One Chinese handheld has a constant discharge if the battery is left on. This lowers the voltage down below the point at which the radio would normally close down, hence it won't power up.

Putting a small piece of insulation tape over the terminals when you fit the battery means it is always fully charged if you store it, in the car for example. Then it is an easy job to remove the battery pack and take off the tape when you want to use it. You should always cover the battery terminals with insulation tape when you store it to prevent short circuits too.

Another useful tip is to buy some adaptors that allow you to connect a PL-259 plug to your BNC or SMA connector on the handheld. These are quite cheap, but means that you can use your home base station antenna on your handheld.

Make sure you get the right one though – some Chinese handhelds have a reverse SMA connector.

Mobile operating

Just to finish, we should really say a few words about mobile operating. That is, operating from your car or other vehicle.

It can be easy to install a 2m/70cm antenna on the roof of your vehicle, especially if it is magnetically-mounted.

Mounting your radio so that it is safe may be slightly more difficult, especially as modern cars seem to have little room on their dashboards. You also have to think about wiring it in – it is usually best to wire the radio direct to the battery, but make sure you have the correctly fused power leads.

Technically it is not illegal to use an amateur radio while driving, but it is fraught with difficulties. Firstly, from a safety aspect, you should always use a hands-free microphone with an appropriate press to talk (PTT) switch. You may have heard that it is technically not illegal to use a hand microphone if you are using amateur radio equipment. However, if you have an accident while operating your radio you could be prosecuted for driving without due care and attention, or careless driving.

The best advice is not to operate your radio when driving, as your full attention may not be on the road ahead. Far better to park up and do some 'static mobile' operating. That way, you are not diverting your attention from the road and you can concentrate on enjoying your hobby. It also means that you could pick a spot that is better suited to VHF/UHF operation, such as the top of a hill. Operating close to the sea on the east or south coasts can also be fruitful, as you often get 'ducting' across the English Channel or North Sea. When that happens it is perfectly possible to work into France or the Netherlands.

All-in-all, just make sure that you are operating safely and within the law.

What can you expect to work?

As we said earlier, you can expect to get perhaps 2-5 miles with a handheld VHF or UHF transceiver, or perhaps 10-20 miles if operating from your car.

From home, generally speaking the higher your antenna is mounted the better your reception will be. From base-to-base you may manage 15-25 miles on 2m FM, depending on your power and the antennas you are both using.

If you are using a repeater the distances can improve dramatically. If you were 20 miles to the east of a repeater, you could probably work someone who was 20 miles to the west of it, bringing the total distance to about 40 miles.

All these distances are rough estimates and based on conditions being average. As you will read in the section on propagation, a tropospheric 'lift' or enhancement, usually connected with a high pressure weather system, can improve the distances you are able to work quite dramatically. Under the right conditions you may be able to work hundreds of miles on VHF or UHF.

Another way of improving the distances you can work is to use single side band (SSB) instead of frequency modulation (FM). SSB is a very efficient mode and you can usually work 50-100% further with SSB. It is particularly useful during lift conditions when UK radio amateurs regularly work continental stations, even with 10W or less.

A small VHF/UHF magnetic mount antenna can easily be fixed to the roof of your car.

Getting Started in Amateur Radio

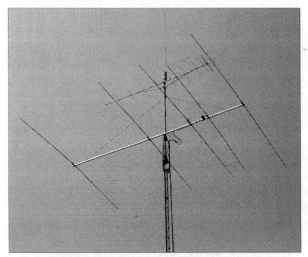

Horizontally-polarised Yagi beam antennas are best for long-distance SSB contacts on VHF.

SSB operators invariably use horizontal polarisation though, so you may need to use a different antenna to the one you use for local FM work. A small beam, such as a five or seven-element Yagi, can work really well.

Amateur radio operation, especially on VHF/UHF, is all about making sure that ALL the components of your station are optimised. That is, that you have the right radio, the best antenna (mounted as high as possible) and fed with the best coaxial cable. Then you have to make sure that you are operating under the best conditions for good propagation. Put all those factors together and VHF/UHF can be a *lot* of fun.

We will take a look at your first QSO (conversation) on VHF/UHF in Chapter 7.

Chapter 4.
Your first HF radio

Choosing an HF radio

If you want to talk to people around the world you will generally need to buy an HF transceiver (transmitter/receiver). Typically, these transmit on all the amateur bands from 160m (1.8MHz) to 10m (28MHz), and often 6m (50MHz) too.

There are one or two lightweight portable transceivers around for HF, typically running 5-10W. These can be ideal if you wish to operate portable outdoors, but if your budget will run to it you might want to consider a 100W-capable base-station transceiver.

An HF radio will let you work the world on the shortwave bands.

Even if your licence doesn't currently allow you to run 100W, a base station can be a good investment and you can usually reduce the power to the 10W or 50W maximum that you are allowed with your current licence. Who knows, you might upgrade your licence within a short period of time and want the extra power.

In addition to being able to transmit on all the HF amateur bands (and each one has different characteristics), you will also be able to use it for listening to other shortwave transmissions from around the world, including broadcast stations, VOLMET (weather), aircraft, and much more.

As for which model to buy, your best bet is to visit an amateur radio equipment supplier, explain what you want to do with the radio and let them suggest a suitable transceiver.

Then, if possible, ask if you can try using the transceiver to see if you can get used to its controls and the way it works. This is important, as we are all different and all have a different idea of what is good and bad. Failing that, see if a member of your local club can demonstrate his or her radio to you.

Getting Started in Amateur Radio

Buying a used transceiver

New equipment has a number of advantages – including a full manufacturer's warranty – but to cut costs it is possible to buy second-hand equipment.

There are some real bargains out there, but beware though – some private sales may not always represent good value and radios can hide faults that are not immediately apparent.

This is why buying a used radio from a radio dealer can make a lot of sense. For starters the radio will have been checked out before it was put on sale. Plus you will probably get some form of warranty as well. If you ask, there is a good chance that you will be able to test the radio too. Prices may be higher than you would pay privately, but what price can you put on peace of mind?

If you don't want to buy from a dealer, or they don't have what you want, you could buy privately. Prices are likely to be cheaper, but 'buyer beware' – you probably won't get any form of warranty at all.

Possibly the best thing is to buy from someone in your local club. If you have problems, at least you can contact them easily. Make sure you find out why they are selling the rig – often it is because they are upgrading and want to dispose of the older radio.

If you are unsure, ask one of the other club members to go along with you to check it out. Most radio amateurs are honest and don't want to get a bad reputation in their area, although there always exceptions.

If you get the chance, try the radio on as many bands as possible, both on receive and transmit. Do you get good signal reports? Is there any sign of a burning smell? Does the radio come with the original packaging and handbook? If not, this may indicate it is stolen, although many people don't keep original boxes nowadays. And, most important, do all the buttons and functions work correctly?

Perhaps the worst way of buying a radio is via an online auction site. The photographs seldom do the radio justice and some descriptions can leave a lot to be desired. Phrases like 'a few scratches' can mean different things to different people and many people have had shocks on opening packages after buying things on auction sites. Plus, you don't get the chance to try the radio before buying – it could hide a multitude of problems that will cost a small fortune to put right.

Many people do successfully buy equipment from online auction sites, but if you do go down this route check the description carefully and be prepared to ask further questions if need be. If the seller is local to you, ask if you can see and test the radio before the auction ends.

What do all the rig's buttons do?

A modern HF radio is a marvel of technology, but often they are so complex that a lot of the controls never get touched! Or if they do, people are unsure what exactly they do and how to use them incorrectly, so let's look at some of the functions on a modern HF radio and how you can use them.

Squelch
Anyone coming from a CB background will be pretty familiar with the squelch control. It

basically turns off the receive audio on the radio until a strong enough signal opens it. Squelch can be very useful (if not essential), as the continuous hiss of a blank FM channel can be very annoying – and we do use FM at the top of the 10m band.

Squelch is used somewhat less on AM and SSB, as the background noise is generally quieter, but there is no reason why you couldn't use it. If you are monitoring a specific frequency on your radio for hours on end it can be useful to squelch the audio on SSB to help retain your sanity, and hearing!

At first glance a modern HF rig's controls can look bewildering.

Noise Reduction
The HF bands can be quite noisy at times and digital noise reduction can be a way of making the audio easier on the ears. The best approach is to engage the noise reduction button and then advance the noise reduction gain knob until you get the effect you are looking for. If you advance it too far the chances are that you will end up with very muddy audio, sounding like someone has their head in a bucket!

Notch / Auto Notch
If you have a whistle or tone on your received signal a notch filter can be used to remove it. The tone can be due to a heterodyne of two signals mixing, or someone tuning up with a carrier. The approach is to switch on the notch filter and rotate the control until the tone vanishes or is attenuated. If the tone frequency changes you will need to re-adjust the control.

Some radios have an auto notch feature that can automatically track tones and remove them without you needing to touch the controls.

A notch filter can adversely affect the quality of the received audio, so it shouldn't be left switched in if it is not required. Also, listening to a CW or PSK 31 transmission with auto notch engaged can be totally self-defeating, as the rig will do its best to remove the very signal you are trying to listen to!

RIT
Receiver Incremental Tuning or Receiver Independent Tuning is a way of changing the frequency your radio is listening to, without affecting the transmit frequency. It can be very useful on SSB if someone comes back to your CQ call and is not quite on your frequency.

By engaging the RIT and adjusting the control slightly you can make their voice sound more intelligible. If you moved the main VFO dial to do this the chances are that they would then change their radio and you would be back where you started.

The only problem with RIT is forgetting that you have engaged it. If you then subsequently move up or down the band to call someone else you will be off frequency. So either switch it off or set it to 0.00kHz offset.

AGC

The Automatic Gain Control is often misunderstood. Received radio signals can vary wildly in their strength, from very weak to incredibly strong. With AGC the radio will try to adjust itself to deal with these vastly differing signal strengths.

On the whole it does a good job, but you can help it. Usually you can choose between fast AGC and slow AGC. This affects the speed at which the radio will adjust itself when listening to different signals. While slow or medium AGC may be fine for SSB transmissions, you may find with CW or PSK31 that you miss the first one or two characters of a transmission as the AGC fails to react quickly enough when moving from a strong signal to a weak one.

Fast AGC tends to work better with digital modes, but it is worth experimenting. AGC can be a personal thing – I prefer a slow setting.

Width Control

All rigs work in different ways, but many will let you adjust the width of the IF filter. Other older radios may have different crystal filters that have the same net effect. These effectively cut down how much of the "band" you listen to at once.

Typical values for SSB tend to be 3.6kHz or 2.7kHz. The first setting is a broad filter that will give you excellent received audio quality. However, if the band is busy you may find that you suffer from adjacent channel interference and the 2.7kHz setting might be better. With most modern radios you can even narrow this down even more, but if you go much below 2.4kHz the audio quality will start to deteriorate. If your radio lets you set up three different width settings for SSB, 3.6, 2.7 and 2.4kHz would be a good choice.

For CW and digital modes you might want to opt for narrower filters. CW enthusiasts usually go for 500Hz or 300Hz, although modern Software Defined Radios (SDR) can even be used down to about 50 or 25Hz on CW with no 'ringing'. Other people prefer to engage a 1000Hz filter, so they can also hear other stations that might be close by, using their brain to filter out the different signals.

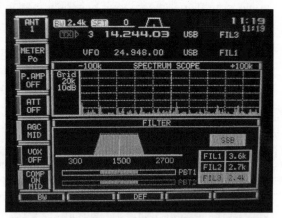

Modern radios let you adjust the filter bandwidth on receive via digital signal processing (DSP).

The correct filter for digital modes, such as RTTY and PSK 31, will depend upon the mode itself and how busy the band is. A good choice would be set up three – say 1000Hz, 750Hz and 500Hz – and select whatever works best for you at the time. But setting a 3.6kHz width would also let you hear signals that are close by, but not on your frequency.

First steps - What can you expect to work?

With an HF radio the world is really your oyster. With the right antenna and right conditions you can work across the globe, but you have to learn how to 'drive' the radio properly first and it will really pay to have a listen to all the bands to get a feel for them.

Years ago most radio amateurs did a long spell as a short wave listener before they got on the air. That is still a good way to learn more about the hobby, to learn the procedures that people use and generally understand how it all works. So we recommend you take some time to listen to each band in turn, to see how people operate and just how far you might able to get. To start you off, here is a rundown of each of the common bands, their characteristics and what you may be able to work.

MF/HF – band by band

1.8MHz (160m) – 1.810 to 2.000MHz

The 1.8MHz band (or Top Band as it is sometimes called) is one of the most difficult and challenging HF/MF bands for any new ham. The reasons for this are numerous, but include the need for plenty of space for an antenna and the particular propagation characteristics of the band.

In the UK the allocation for amateur radio is 1.810-2.000MHz. To familiarise yourself with it we suggest you take a look at the band plan on the RSGB website. For telephony (speech), it runs from 1.843 to 2.000MHz.

Foundation licensees are limited to 10W (10dBW). Intermediate licensees can run up to 50W (17 dBW) from 1.810 to 1.850MHz and then just 32W (15dBW) from 1.850 to 2.000MHz. Full licence holders can use 400W up to 1.850MHz but are also limited to 32W from 1.850 to 2.000MHz.

Note that radio amateurs are not the exclusive users of the frequency range 1.850 to 2.000MHz and we can only use 1.810 to 1.830MHz on the basis of non-interference to other services outside the UK.

So, having got that out of the way, what can you actually work?

Propagation on 1.8MHz is limited to local contacts (say, around 50 miles maximum) during the day, but DX is possible at night, especially around sunrise and sunset. You will need a good antenna to get much further than Europe and there can be a lot of interference. That's what makes 1.8MHz a challenge.

1.8MHz is a good winter band, but not so good in the summer – when the nights are short and ionospheric absorption is high.

Unlike the higher HF bands, long distance propagation is often better around sunspot minimum, when solar activity and therefore noise levels are lower.

Efficient 1.8MHz antennas tend to be huge. With a wavelength of 160m, even a half wave dipole is going to be around 80m (264ft) long. This makes life difficult, unless you have plenty of real estate.

Fortunately there are ways of getting on 160m that don't require that amount of space. One way is to

Even a 'short' vertical for 1.8MHz can be 18m (60ft) tall.

Getting Started in Amateur Radio

use a quarter wave inverted L, with a total length of about 40m (132ft), fed against a good earth. This is what Stew Perry W1BB, a well known advocate of 1.8MHz, recommended to newcomers.

Another 'get you on the band' antenna can be made by strapping the inner and outer of the feeder on an existing 80m antenna, such as a dipole, G5RV or W5GI dipole, and feeding that against earth using a suitable ATU. The earth could be a combination of ground stakes and as many long radials as you can physically put down. It may not be a contest winner, but it will get you on the band.

The best way to find out about 1.8MHz is to listen, listen and listen again. You may hear many semi-local UK QSOs on lower side band (LSB) towards the top end of the band. The serious DXers can be found at the bottom, invariably using Morse code to make their contacts.

3.5MHz (80m) – 3.500 to 3.800MHz

3.5MHz can offer a lot for radio amateurs – many use it as a local chat band on lower side band (LSB) and there are lots of nets for special interest groups. But the long, dark winter nights can also turn it into a DX band. In autumn, winter and early spring 80m is ideal for near vertical incidence skywave (NVIS) communications around the UK.

Expect to be able to make ground wave contacts out to around 50 miles or so, and NVIS sky-wave contacts beyond that up to several hundred miles, as long as the critical frequency stays high enough. The critical frequency is that which will just return signals back to earth if they are directed straight up.

In winter, start to look for DX on 80m to the East during the late afternoon, and to the West up to and just past sunrise. The best place to look for SSB DX on 80m is in the top 5-10kHz of the band, where there are often nets in progress. Many amateurs have worked their first US and Canadian stations on the band in this way.

3.5MHz really starts to shine as a DX band after sunset in the winter.

For the best DX on 80m you need a dark (night-time) path between you and the other station. To make this easier to visualise you can use a computer program, such as Sunclock, or perhaps one of the propagation programs like W6ELProp, ACE-HF or VOAProp. There are various internet sites that will also show you the same information – just search Google for Sunclock.

Look out for sunrise enhancements too. Start to look around 60 minutes before the sun rises and keep going until around 60 minutes after sunrise.

In general, the best conditions will occur in the early hours of the morning, with DX being workable as far afield as the mid-western USA, the Middle East and

A computer program like Sunclock can help you visualise which paths may be open on 3.5MHz (80m).

Asia, depending upon the efficiency of your antenna.

3.5MHz is less good at times of high sunspot activity and also in the summer (when absorption can be high).

5MHz (60m) – segments from 5.2585 to 5.4065MHz

5MHz is an oddball 'band'. I say 'band' in inverted commas as it isn't a full band as such, just segments of frequencies. The lowest frequency is 5.2585MHz and the highest is 5.4065MHz. In between are 11 small segments or blocks allocated for different uses, such as SSB, CW, beacons, and digital modes.

These are all allocated on a secondary basis to holders of a 5MHz Notice of Variation (NoV) for the UK Full Amateur Licence. The maximum power output on 5MHz is currently restricted to 100 Watts from the transmitter.

Please note you can't currently use 5MHz if you have a Foundation or Intermediate licence. You must have a Full or Advanced licence.

The best thing to do is study the 5MHz bandplan at www.rsgb.org for the latest news.

But what can you work? 5MHz is a very good band for working around the UK, using near vertical incidence skywave (NVIS) communications. DXing used to be frowned upon, and there were very few countries to work anyway, but many other countries do now have a 5MHz allocation. These days 5.2585MHz is set aside for international use.

There are also a number of beacons on the band, including the UK's own set on 5.290MHz (GB3RAL, GB3ORK and GB3WES), which have been used extensively for propagation experiments.

Because other countries' use of 5MHz changes quite regularly, if you are interested in the band it is worth keeping an eye on the Wikipedia entry for 5MHz and also joining the 'ukfivemegs' Yahoo group.

7MHz (40m) – 7.000 to 7.200MHz

7MHz is a great band, as it is usually open 24 hours a day. It should be open to European stations during daylight hours and you may be able to work other UK stations too, especially at times of high sunspot activity. At sunspot minimum though, closer stations might be inaudible on 40m and you would be better off heading towards 3.5MHz. This is due to the low critical frequencies, which means your NVIS (near vertical incidence skywave) or high-angle signals that are needed to talk to close-in stations are not being reflected back to earth, but continue into outer space.

If the critical frequency is lower than 7MHz you will find it difficult to work stations in a radius of up to 150-200 miles from you, while you will still be able to work stations further afield. This is due to the lower angle that the radio waves hit the ionosphere.

But local daytime contacts are not just what 40m is really good at – its DX potential is what attracts people to the band, especially in late autumn and the winter.

7MHz can start to open for DX in the afternoon in late autumn and remain open to DX until after the sun has risen the following morning. In fact, the first 60 minutes after sunrise in the winter on 40m is not called the 'Golden Hour' for nothing.

7MHz starts to open-up to DX in an easterly direction and to Scandinavia in the late afternoon and will get stronger after sunset. Propagation will swing around as night progresses, during which time Africa should be possible too. Later in the evening propagation will start to go 'long', as the critical frequency drops and a lot of the European QRM diminishes, leaving more DX signals.

In winter you also have a good shot at the North-East coast of Canada and Newfoundland from around 1700-1800hrs and onward until the early hours. This path may peak again at sunrise and onwards until about 0900hrs. After sunrise the interference (QRM) from European stations to the East of us is greatly reduced, making it easier for us to work stations to the West.

7MHz can sound like a very busy band and while there is no doubt that CW (Morse) will increase your chances of working DX on 40m, do try with SSB.

Malcolm, G3PDH regularly works a hundred or more stations on 40m when running a special event station.

10MHz (30m) – 10.100 to 10.140MHz

10MHz is an odd band in that it is used for Morse and digital modes, but not SSB. You may read that it shares the characteristics of both 40m and 20m, and indeed it does. 14MHz is predominantly a daylight band, closing after dark in the winter as the MUF (Maximum Useable Frequency) drops. 7MHz on the other hand is generally not much of a DX band during the day, but comes alive after dark.

As 10MHz sits between these two bands the frequency is mostly too high for local contacts – high angle signals won't be returned to earth – but you should be able to work around Europe. At sunspot maximum it may support local contacts during the day, when signals are returned from local stations via the ionosphere; but at night in the winter, when 20m may be closing you could find that 30m remains open longer, much as 40m does.

This is what makes 30m such a fascinating band – it can be open to somewhere virtually 24 hours a day, whereas 20m is often closed during the night and 40m won't get far during the day thanks to D-layer absorption.

The other good news is that, on the whole, you won't be fighting stations with massive beam antennas. An efficient antenna - a half-wave dipole - is only 15m long.

14MHz (20m) – 14.000 to 14.350MHz

If you have just received your licence and are finding your way around the HF bands, a good place to start might be 14MHz.

Why? Well, this band is probably the most active and consistent band in terms of being able to hear and work DX – long distance contacts.

While 21MHz (15m) and above are predominantly daylight bands, at some times of the year you will find that 20m can be open around the clock.

Yes, in the winter it tends to close after dark, but as we head into summer you may find that it stays open a lot longer. This is due to the nuances of ionospheric propagation, which means that it is possible to work DX in the evening when you get home from work.

14MHz propagation tends to follow the sun. In the morning you may hear stations to the East of you – typically Russia, the Far East, Australia and even New Zealand if you are lucky.

As the earth rotates propagation can shift towards the South, so you get good paths into parts of Africa, even South Africa. In the afternoon you will find that the propagation shifts yet again, and North/South America comes through.

In terms of what else you might hear, apart from CW at the bottom end of the band, you have PSK data at about 14.070MHz and RTTY at about 14.080MHz. And don't forget the International Beacon Project beacons on 14.100MHz, which we talk about later.

14MHz is often used by special event stations too, as it provides reliable communication, regardless of where we are in the sunspot cycle.

Image: TX5G, Clipperton Island/Cordell Expeditions.

14MHz is a favourite band for DXpeditions, because it promises the possibility of worldwide contacts at almost any point of the sunspot cycle.

If you are interested in DX there are also a whole host of worldwide nets that tend to congregate around the band. These can give you a good chance of hearing (and possibly working) some exotic stations.

14MHz also supports 'long path' contacts, whereby signals go the long way around the earth instead of taking the shortest route (short path). This can happen at certain times of the day/year and gives us reliable paths, such as the UK to New Zealand on 20m in the morning.

From May to the end of August you may also experience some Sporadic-E (Es) openings. Although we normally associate these with 28MHz and 50MHz they often occur on 14MHz. It is just that we tend not to notice them as much, due to the other more general F-layer ionospheric propagation taking place.

Sporadic-E can give you very strong contacts around Europe and occasionally further afield.

18MHz (17m) – 18.068 to 18.168MHz

18MHz has similar propagation to 14MHz, but it has a totally different feel. It is not a contest band and QSOs tend to be longer and more chatty. For this reason many people say that 18MHz is a very friendly band.

Unlike 14MHz and 21MHz, a lot of stations are not using beams on 18MHz, which means you have a much better chance of working around the world with a simple antenna.

Propagation wise it is similar to 14MHz and 21MHz. That is, the autumn, winter and spring are the best times and the band is predominantly open to DX in daylight. It can be expected to close at night, apart from at times of high solar flux.

One advantage of the higher HF bands is that the antennas tend to be smaller than those needed on 160, 80 and 40m.

21MHz (15m) – 21.000 to 21.450MHz

21MHz is a band that can offer a lot – antennas are smaller than those used on 14MHz and you have 450kHz of bandwidth to play with. D-layer absorption is less than it is on the lower bands and noise levels tend to be lower too, which means you can hear stations even if they are very weak. Try doing that on 3.5MHz!

It is an excellent DX band during the day, but it is often overlooked as people rush to 28MHz, in the hope that it too will be open. The good news is that when the sun isn't quite playing ball and 28MHz is dead, it may be that 21MHz is alive – it is worth checking.

At night though, as solar ionisation drops off, 21MHz will often close until the morning. Another problem with 21MHz is that it really needs a fairly high solar flux to come alive in the first place. That isn't to say that there aren't good openings on when solar flux levels are low, but they may often be weak or short lived.

On this band you will definitely find that a good antenna helps. Long wires, G5RVs and Windoms (OCF dipoles) are not their best on 21MHz and will likely be beaten by even a half-wave dipole at 25-35ft.

24MHz (12m) – 24.890 to 24.990MHz

Like 10MHz and 18MHz, 24MHz was given to radio amateurs in 1979 at the World Administrative Radio Conference. That's why these three bands are sometimes referred to as the 'WARC' bands. Covering 24.890 to 24.990MHz, it offers some great qualities.

Firstly, it is quite high in frequency, so noise is not as big a problem as it is on the lower bands. In fact, at my quite noisy suburban location the average noise level on 24MHz is about S1, compared with about S9 on 3.5MHz and S8 on 7MHz. This makes it much easier to hear weak signals.

At the same time, the band is low enough in frequency to benefit from F2 layer openings with relatively low levels of solar flux, often at times when 28MHz is closed.

DX openings are quite possible on 24MHz, even at sunspot minimum. Having said that, they are likely to be sparse, fleeting and unreliable.

A good starting point to check for openings is the NCDXF beacon chain on 24.930MHz. In three minutes you can find out if there is any propagation to many parts of the world. We will look more closely at this later in the book.

Like 28MHz, the band is likely to be closed at night, other than for ground wave propagation to local hams, out to around 15-20 miles. After sunrise the band will be slow to open, as F-layer ionisation builds up. If the band opens at all it will be at its best by early afternoon, but by dusk it will close down again for the night.

24MHz is a band that really benefits from higher sunspot numbers, but in the meantime it has another trick up its sleeve – Sporadic-E, which begins to show itself in May and continues throughout the summer.

While the factors behind Sporadic-E are not well understood, we know what its effects are on radio signals. In summer (in the Northern hemisphere) clouds of ionised gases can form in the lower (90-100km) E-region of the ionosphere. These are difficult to predict and are fast moving, often measured at up to 160km/h or more. They are, however, very intense and capable of reflecting/refracting radio waves of frequencies of up to 144MHz. You can find out more about Sporadic-E in the chapter on propagation.

In general, under Sporadic-E conditions, you should be able to work stations up to a distance of around 1200-1400miles. The signals will be strong, with S9+ commonplace. At times there will be rapid fading (QSB) though, and you may be able to see the effects of the fast moving E's clouds as signals from one area are replaced by those from another in just a few minutes.

If you are very lucky, and especially if you have a beam, you could benefit from multi-hop Sporadic-E, whereby your signals are reflected off one cloud, bounce of the ground or the sea and then reflect back off a further cloud to their ultimate destination.

28MHz (10m) – 28.000 to 29.700MHz

28MHz is a real enigma. At times of high sunspot activity it can be open to all parts of the world during the day. As absorption is very low, even weak signals that are close to the noise level can often be worked with ease.

This makes it the ultimate DX band, even with low powers, such as the 10W permitted with the Foundation licence. However, when we get to sunspot minimum, the band can be devoid of signals for very long periods.

The moral is simple; when we are at or near a sunspot maximum, use 28MHz as much as you can.

The band also offers a lot of open space for different modes and techniques. There are a lot of low power beacons on 28MHz and a 5W beacon transmitting from the midwest of the United States can be quite easy to hear in the UK near sunspot maximum.

28MHz also has a dedicated FM portion, at the top end of the band (29.5 to 29.7MHz) with lots of repeaters around the world. The KQ2H repeater in upstate New York on 29.620MHz, for example, can romp into the UK during the afternoons in the autumn and winter.

Sporadic-E can also be prevalent from May to August, bringing lots of extremely strong European stations to the band, just like 24MHz.

People who have heard 28MHz in full swing are unlikely to forget it, but at sunspot minimum you may wonder what all the fuss is about.

Chapter 5. Other equipment you might need

As well as a radio (transceiver) and an antenna you will need a few other pieces of equipment for your radio room or 'shack'.

Here is a list of the main items:

Power Supply Unit (PSU)

If you are using a handheld transceiver on VHF or UHF FM you will probably use rechargeable batteries, but if you want to operate the radio without batteries (in your house, for example), you may want to invest in a small DC power supply. You will need to check what voltage your handheld works on, because not all of

Modern switch-mode 12v power supplies are very small and lightweight.

them run on 13.8V. Some have an adaptor that you can buy that will let you run it off a 13.8V supply – it is worth checking.

If you are using a mobile or base station radio you are likely to need a 13.8V power supply, although some base stations have their own built-in mains power supply.

The maximum current that the radio will need should be listed in the radio's instructions, but a typical 100W HF radio might require up to 20-23 Amps. It is best to get a power supply that can comfortably deliver this level of current.

Your equipment will only draw the current it needs, so you can quite happily buy a power supply that is more powerful than required, indeed it can be advantageous as you might want to upgrade to a more powerful radio in the future.

There are two main types of power supply on the market – linear and switched-mode. The linear type uses a bulky transformer – along with control circuitry – to change the 230V mains voltage to 13.8V DC. Such power supplies tend to be large and heavy, especially the high-current models.

Switch-mode power supplies use a different approach. In a switch-mode power supply the AC voltage is converted directly to DC and filtered. This high-voltage DC is fed to a power oscillator that 'switches' it on and off at high rate – usually somewhere between 20kHz and 500kHz. The result is pulsating DC that can be applied to a much smaller transformer, for conversation to 13.8V.

The advantages of the switch-mode power supply are that it can be made smaller, lighter, and usually less expensive. The disadvantage of the switch-mode design is that some can generate interference signals that you can hear on your radio. If you're considering buying a switch-mode power supply, look for models that boast low 'RFI' (Radio Frequency Interference).

Some switch-mode power supplies have a small knob that you can turn, to move any interference away from the frequency you are listening on.

Co-ax

You will need some cable to connect your transceiver to your antenna. Most radios are designed with a 50-ohm unbalanced output, which matches with 50-ohm coaxial cable.

Something you should think about is the quality of the coax and its inherent losses. Generally speaking, the higher you go in frequency, the greater the losses become.

If you are only operating on the lower HF bands and at modest power, thin (5mm-diameter) RG58 coax might suffice, as long as the run isn't too long, but if you are using high power, the higher HF bands (24-28MHz), or 144/430MHz you will need to use better quality coax.

Coaxial cable comes in different thicknesses and quality. This is RG-213, suitable for use on HF and VHF.

For general HF use, RG213 is a good choice. It is thicker than RG58 and less flexible, but it offers much lower losses. It is also OK for use on 2m (144MHz) and 70cm (430MHz), although there are now better alternatives.

Newer coax types like WestFlex, Ecoflex, Aircell and Aircom Plus are better suited to VHF/UHF use, but cost more than RG213.

We take a closer look at coaxial cable and other feedlines in the next chapter.

SWR meter / Antenna Analyser

Many modern radios have built-in SWR meters, which are essential when setting up antennas. Also, many external antenna tuning units also have built-in SWR meters that make it easier to find a match.

If you are putting a radio into a car you will definitely need to beg or borrow an SWR meter, to set up the antenna correctly.

If your radio doesn't have a built-in meter and you are setting up a home-base antenna, an SWR meter can also be handy. When buying one make sure it covers the bands you require, because some only cover HF and don't work on VHF and above.

If you are keen on experimenting with antennas an antenna analyser can be a good investment. They are not cheap, but they will tell you far more than just an antenna's SWR. Some will give you graphical displays of the SWR curve of an antenna, allow you to detect faults in cables, measure cable length 'electrically' and give information about an antenna's reactance.

Antenna analysers are not for complete beginners and you might be better off in the first instance with a basic SWR meter.

An antenna analyser can be invaluable, especially if you enjoy experimenting a lot with antennas.

Log book

It is no longer essential for you to keep a log (a written record) of all your contacts. However, most radio amateurs find log books very useful. Not only can you keep note of your contacts and the countries you have worked, but it can come in useful if there are any complaints about interference – because your log will tell you and Ofcom what band you were on, or even if you weren't transmitting at all!

A paper log is inexpensive and easy to keep, but ultimately you might want to consider a computer log. Software is available for both PCs and Macs and varies from completely free to paid for.

The advantage of an electronic log is that it can automatically keep tabs on whom you have worked and on what bands. It can also tell you if you have worked someone before and remind you of the other operator's name.

Most electronic logging software packages will also print labels for your QSL cards, keep track of your progress on any awards you are chasing, upload information to the American Radio Relay League's 'Logbook of the World' system and much more.

We'll look at electronic logs and QSL cards later.

An electronic logbook can be invaluable, especially if you are chasing awards. This is 'Logger32', which is free.

Chapter 6.
Practical antennas

The most important part of any amateur radio station is the antenna. You can have the most advanced transceiver in the world, but if you can't radiate a decent signal you won't be heard.

And because antennas are reciprocal – they generally receive as well as they transmit – a good antenna will let you hear more as well.

Although you could hear a broadcast radio station by sticking any old piece of wire in the antenna socket of a receiver, amateur radio needs a more scientific approach.

You don't have to use a large antenna like this Force 12 XR6 Yagi on HF, but it certainly helps.

What exactly is an antenna?

An antenna is just a metallic element that intercepts electromagnetic waves that are passing by, converting them into a tiny electrical current that your receiver can amplify and turn into an audio signal. When used for transmitting, we apply a high-frequency AC electrical signal to the antenna, which in turn results in electromagnetic waves being radiated by it.

For an antenna to work well it ideally needs to be mounted as high up and in the clear as possible. This will maximise its ability to radiate a signal properly. It will also minimise the pickup of unwanted electrical noise. Unfortunately electrical noise is commonplace these days, a lot of it being thanks to the proliferation of electronic devices and cheap power supplies, such as the tiny chargers used for mobile phones and tablet PCs. The greater the distance you can place between your antenna and any noise source, the better.

The antenna also needs to be the correct size for the frequency upon which we are operating. In other words, it needs to be 'tuned' to the frequency we are operating on, much as an organ pipe is tuned to the frequency of the note you wish to produce.

Many antennas are designed to work on more than one frequency, which means you don't have to have a separate antenna for each band.

Feeders

We connect an antenna to a transceiver using a length of antenna feeder or transmission line. We want it to introduce as little loss as possible, so that our signals (both transmitted and received) are not attenuated. We also want the feeder not to pick up any unwanted noise, which could make a weak signal even harder to hear.

There are two basic types of feeder – coaxial cable and open wire.

Coaxial cable (or coax) has an inner conductor, surrounded by a tubular insulating layer. This in turn is surrounded by a tubular conducting shield. The whole is then wrapped in an insulating sleeve. Coaxial cable was invented by English engineer and mathematician Oliver Heaviside, who patented the design in 1880.

The relative dimensions of the cable are carefully controlled, to give a precise, constant conductor spacing. This is needed for it to function efficiently as a radio frequency transmission line. This in turn gives it a characteristic impedance.

For amateur radio we tend to use 50-ohm coax, as that gives the best match to our radios (which are designed for a 50-ohm output). You may not be familiar with the term impedance, but it is a measure of how something reacts to an alternating current, such as the high frequency signals we apply to our antenna.

As was said in the last chapter, coax is commonly used for VHF and UHF antennas. It comes in different diameters. For example, RG58 is 5mm in diameter and RG213 is 10mm. There are also lots of different designs of coax cable, some offering a lot less loss, but at a price.

The losses tend to increase as you go up in frequency, so a coax type that could be useful on, say, 160m (1.8MHz) might be way too lossy at 70cm (433MHz). It also pays to keep coax runs as short as possible, because the losses are a function of the length too.

When choosing coax for your installation, make sure you choose the optimum type for the bands you wish to operate on.

There is also another type of feeder called open-wire feeder or 'twin' feeder. This isn't used quite so much nowadays, but it has its uses, especially on HF where it can offer very low loss over long distances.

Twin feeder comprises two parallel conductors, with a fixed distance between them.

The currents flowing in the open wire feeder are equal and opposite, so the resultant fields around the feeder cancel each other out and no signal is radiated.

Modern 300-ohm feeder comes in slotted and unslotted forms. This is the slotted variety.

The bad news is that open wire feeder needs to be kept well away from metal objects and doesn't lend itself to being squeezed through window frames or holes in walls.

Open wire feeder is available commercially, in both 300-ohm or 450-ohm impedance varieties. The most common type is 'slotted' feeder, with holes cut into the centre insulation to stop rain water collecting.

You can also make twin feeder yourself, but you need to work out how to keep the two wires the correct distance apart and ensure that the feeder is supported properly and doesn't degrade in the sun.

RF Plugs

Before you can use an antenna you need to connect your feeder to it – and then screw the plug into the radio. Radio equipment uses specific plugs, made for the job. You can't just strip off the end of the coax and push it into the socket. You need the right plug.

Most base station and mobile radios use something called an SO-239 socket on the back, which mates to a PL-259 plug on the coax. PL-259s come in different sizes, to fit the coax type you are using. They can be quite cheap, but it pays to spend a little more to get quality plugs. Then, you have to learn how to fit them properly.

It is essential that you learn how to 'dress' the coax properly, so that the plug screws onto the coax braid, leaving the centre conductor to protrude through the plug's centre pin. Then you need to solder the centre of the coax to

PL259 plugs are used to connect coaxial cable to radios transceivers and antenna tuning units.

the pin, otherwise you could end up with a dodgy joint that becomes intermittent. PL-259s are also made that crimp onto coaxial cable.

The best way to learn how to fit a PL-259 is to Google it, and watch one of the excellent videos on YouTube that shows someone actually doing it.

Finally, if the plug is going to be outdoors, it needs to properly waterproofed. The best material for this is self-amalgamating tape, which bonds to itself and forms a water-proof seal.

There are other plug types that are used in amateur radio, including N, BNC and SMA. Many handhelds use a BNC or SMA connector, while N-types are most often used at UHF and above.

Each has a particular use and can be quite difficult to fit. Again, that is where Google can be your friend.

What exactly is SWR and why should you be bothered about it?

An important factor when setting-up an antenna is its so-called Standing Wave Ratio (SWR). In technical terms, SWR, or more correctly VSWR (Voltage Standing Wave Ratio) if we are deriving the SWR from measured voltages, shows how much power is being reflected back down a feedline due to an impedance mismatch between the feeder and the antenna.

For example, a typical modern HF transceiver has a characteristic output impedance of 50-ohms. If we connect a length of 50-ohm coax to it and this and, in turn, it is connected to an antenna that has an impedance of 50-ohms we get excellent power transfer from the transceiver to the antenna. We theoretically get little or no power reflected back along the feeder and the SWR would be 1:1. This, we would say, is an excellent match.

However, if the antenna does not present an impedance of 50-ohms (which is often the case) and as a result we have an SWR greater than 1:1, there will be power reflected back down the feeder. It is the interaction of this reflected power with the forward power that causes the standing wave patterns.

So why is high SWR a problem?

Firstly, an SWR of less than 2:1 doesn't usually cause problems to your radio, but if the impedance mismatch produces an SWR much higher than this your radio will start to reduce its output, in an effort to avoid damage to its output transistors due to the high voltages that may start to become present.

This is is why it is important to protect your radio from operating into a high SWR. An Antenna Tuning Unit (ATU) will not make your antenna more efficient, but it will stop your radio reducing its output if the SWR at the feeder is, say, 3:1 or higher.

Getting your antenna to present a good match to your transceiver is a vital part of the set-up process.

But there is another reason to carefully match your antenna to the feeder. As I said earlier, all feed lines, such as coax or open wire, exhibit losses. Figures are quoted by the manufacturers, but they are usually based on the feeder operating with an SWR of 1:1. If the SWR on the feedline is higher than this, the losses can increase dramatically.

For example, if you have 20m of RG58 connected to an antenna with a 1:1 SWR match your losses will be about 1.325dB at 28MHz. Usually we say that 6dB equals about one S point (although many transceivers differ from this). From this you can see that you lose less than half an S point.

But if the coax is connected to a highly mismatched antenna, say with an SWR of 64:1, you will have additional mismatch losses of 9.074dB, bringing the total loss to 10.398dB. Now you would be losing nearly two S points.

The answer is to improve the match to the antenna, to bring it as close as you can to 1:1 – and use better coax too. With 20m of RG213 coax with an SWR of 1:1 the losses would be about 0.5dB at 28MHz (not the 1.325dB you get with RG58).

Open wire feeder exhibits far less loss than coax, even with a high SWR, but you will have to deal with the fact that it is balanced and your radio output is unbalanced. That is, you will have to use a balun (balanced-unbalanced transformer) to connect it the radio. Also, open wire feeder doesn't like being placed near metal objects or laid on the floor, so coax may be a better choice in some circumstances.

One other point, the losses in long lengths of coax make it appear that the SWR at the radio end of the feeder looks better than it really is at the antenna. For this reason, if possible, it is a good idea to measure the SWR at the antenna feedpoint and not at the transceiver end of the feeder. In this way you will have a true indication of what your antenna's SWR is.

SWR can seem a bewildering concept to the beginner, but RSGB has various books that can help you understand it better.

Polarisation

There is one more aspect of antenna theory we need to look at – polarisation.

You might be familiar with Polaroid sunglasses. These only allow light through if the polarisation of the light (the direction of vibration of the light waves) matches the orientation of the Polaroid material.

You can demonstrate this if you hold two Polaroid lenses up, one in front of the other. If you rotate one of them you get to a point where the front lens is only allowing light with one particular polarisation through, while the back lens will only allow light with a polarisation that is 90 degrees different to pass. The net result is that practically no light can pass through the lens pair and the image looks very dark.

Not surprisingly, as radio waves are electromagnetic, they can also be polarised. So, for example, a vertical VHF antenna will emit vertically-polarised radio waves. A horizontal dipole will emit horizontally-polarised radio waves.

This small 'Alexloop' antenna offers vertical polarisation at very low angles and horizontal polarisation at high angles.

If you wish to work on VHF and UHF it pays to ensure you are using the same polarisation as the other station. By convention, we tend to use vertically-polarised antennas on VHF and UHF for FM, and horizontally-polarised antennas (usually beams) for longer distance SSB signals.

If you try to use a vertical antenna for SSB your signals will be severely attenuated when they are received at the other end, so make sure you choose the right antenna and polarisation for the mode you are using.

HF is a little more complex, as any radio signal that is reflected back to the earth by the ionosphere will have had its original polarisation changed. This is because radio waves passing through the ionosphere are split into two separate waves – an ordinary and an extraordinary wave. These combine to give a circular or elliptically-polarised wave when it returns to earth, with the polarisation constantly changing (which is one reason we get fading on HF signals).

For this reason the polarity of your HF

antenna is less important, unless you are listening to a close-in station via ground wave. Amateurs tend to use horizontally-polarised dipoles and beams; but vertically-polarised vertical antennas are also popular, especially on the lower bands. These are chosen as they can give superior low-angle take-off on 80m (3.5MHz) and 40m (7MHz), compared with low horizontal dipoles.

But rest assured, if a station in a far-flung country is transmitting on HF using a vertical antenna, the chances are that you *will* be able to hear him on a horizontally-polarised antenna in the UK, for the reasons already outlined.

Basic antennas

Let's now take a look at a few antennas that you could build and use.

The Half-Wave Dipole

The simplest (and perhaps cheapest) antenna you can build is a half-wave dipole. This is simply cut for your band of choice, according to the chart below, and fed in the middle with 50-ohm coax. Don't be fooled by the simplicity of the antenna – dipoles are very effective and are the standard by which many other antennas are compared.

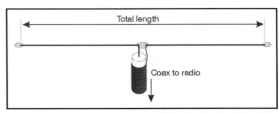

The half-wave dipole.

A half-wave dipole is cut to length according to the formula:
Total length (in feet) = 468/f, where f is the centre frequency in MHz.
The metric formula is total length (in metres) = 142.65/f.

Just about any type of insulated wire will work and you don't necessarily need insulators – just tie small knots in the wire at the outer ends and thread some nylon line through the loop, to tie both ends off to suitable points, such as a tree, fence post or chimney.

A so-called 'chocolate block' electrical connector will let you connect the inner ends of the dipole to your 50-ohm coax. The whole assembly can then be put into a suitable small plastic box, to keep it waterproof.

Make sure you lead the coax away at right angles to the dipole, to prevent RF pickup and help keep the antenna balanced.

If you have completed the Foundation licence training you may recall that it said that if you are connecting coax (unbalanced) to a dipole (balanced) you may need to use a balun or balanced-to-unbalanced transformer.

Frequency (MHz)	Total length (feet/ins)	(metres)
3.650	128ft 2in	39.06m
7.100	65ft 11in	20.09m
10.100	46ft 4in	14.12m
14.175	33ft 0in	10.06m
18.100	25ft 10in	7.88m
21.225	22ft 1in	6.73m
24.940	18ft 9in	5.72m
28.500	16ft 5in	5.00m
29.500	15ft 10in	4.83m
50.200	9ft 4in	2.84m

Typical half-wave dipole lengths.

This is indeed best practice and you can either buy a balun or make one your self using a suitable ferrite toroid, or create a 'choke balun' by closely winding about 8-10 turns of coax on a former about 3 to 4 inches in diameter

In reality though, and with the low power you are likely to use as a Foundation licensee, as long as your coax drops away symmetrically from the antenna (that is, vertically straight down) you may find that you can get away without using a balun.

Once you have installed the antenna, check the SWR in the centre of the band. Now check it at the band edges too. If the SWR is better at the lower edge of the band than the top it means its too long. If it is better at the top end of the band its too short.

You can make a choke balun by coiling your coax on a former and securing it with cable ties or insulating tape.

If its too long don't cut it – just fold the ends back on themselves and either twist the wires together or use nylon cable ties to keep the ends tidy. Folding it back will make it 'electrically shorter' and have the same effect as cutting it.

Don't be surprised to find that you have to shorten an antenna slightly, once you have it in position. The PVC insulation of the wire and capacitive end effects will make it appear too long electrically, and it is easier to shorten an antenna than lengthen it.

One you have the lowest SWR at or around the centre of the band, stop. As long as it is less than about 2:1 you will be fine, although in reality you should be able to get it to 1.5:1 or less.

It is best to mount the centre of the antenna as high as you can. This helps your radiated signal, as it is the current portion of the antenna that does all the work and the current maximum on a half wave dipole is in the centre.

A half-wave dipole is, strictly speaking, a monoband antenna, although a 40m (7MHz) dipole can be used on 15m (21MHz), albeit with a slightly higher SWR. In reality you can use a dipole on almost any band other than the one it was cut for, but to make it work you will need to use an ATU. Under these conditions the performance may not be very good, but as a 'get you going' compromise antenna it will work.

If you really want to a use single dipole on something other than its design frequency you are better off feeding it with 300- or 450-ohm ribbon cable, but bear in mind this is not as easy to handle as coax and must be kept away from metallic objects. Your dipole then becomes a 'tuned doublet'. If you do want to experiment with this type of antenna, cut your dipole for the lowest frequency you want to use and then use it with twin feeder on this and higher frequencies. You will have to use a balanced ATU or a balun to connect the coax from the transceiver to the shack end of your twin feeder.

The G5RV dipole

The G5RV is a popular antenna for radio amateurs who are starting out. It is cheap to buy and easy to build if you want to make your own. It will work adequately on a number of

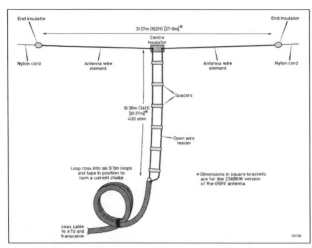

The G5RV is a popular multiband antenna, although it doesn't offer a very good SWR match on a lot of bands.

bands, and get you onto 80m (3.5MHz) with an antenna that is shorter than a full-size 80m dipole.

The antenna was designed by the late Louis Varney, G5RV and consists of a 102ft (31.1m) dipole top with a 28.5ft (8.5m) centre section made out of open wire feeder (or 300-ohm windowed ribbon cable). You then connect your 50-ohm coax to the bottom.

In my book *Stealth Antennas* I go into details as to what the exact length of the 300-ohm matching section should be and why, but if you are buying a commercial G5RV you don't have to worry about it; and if you are building your own, but don't have an antenna analyser, stick with 28.5ft.

You should also really use a choke balun at the base of the matching section too – about 8-10 turns of coax in a six-inch coil should do it.

The antenna was originally designed to be one and a half wavelengths long at 20m (14MHz). I don't think Louis Varney ever really envisaged it as a multiband antenna, and he certainly didn't have access to the WARC bands (10, 18 and 24MHz) that we have now, so let's look at just how good a G5RV is across the bands.

The first thing to say is that if you can install the G5RV so that the top section is perfectly horizontal, do! For the rest of us you may have to have it as an inverted-V, that is, with the apex at a high point, such as on a chimney stack, with the ends coming down to a lower level. I tried a G5RV as an inverted-V as this QTH and while it fitted the space quite well I was very disappointed with its performance. It performed about as well as any other antenna on 80m, but on HF DX it was pretty awful.

The table on the left shows the SWR readings I got in real life, with a G5RV installed as an inverted-V at the end of 30ft of RG213 coax.

What you find is that the antenna doesn't offer a good match on any band, but should be within the range of an external ATU on all bands.

If you are stuck with an internal ATU you may struggle, as some cannot cope with SWR figures greater than about 3:1.

In conclusion then, I think the G5RV has won a lot of

Frequency	SWR
3.5MHz	1.7:1
3.6MHz	2.3:1
3.8MHz	5:1
7.0MHz	2.1:1
7.1MHz	2.0:1
10.1MHz	10.2:1
14.150MHz	5.6:1
18.150MHz	3.3:1
21.0MHz	5.4:1
21.450MHz	5.4:1
24.9MHz	6.7:1
28MHz	5.6:1
29MHz	3.6:1

Real life SWR of a G5RV.

followers who use it for a general natter antenna on 80m and as a general do-it-all antenna everywhere else. It doesn't like being configured as an inverted-V (it flattens the radiation pattern and reduces the lobes) and it isn't a good match on any band, although you should be able to match it with an external ATU. Hopefully an internal ATU will cope, especially on 80m and 40m, but some types may struggle on the other bands.

It has to be said that the G5RV is not the 'be all and end all' in terms of all-out performance, but many hams seem happy with it, especially on 80, 40 and 20m.

Take a tip from me. The best way forward is to have an antenna for 80m and 40m, and then a separate antenna(s) for the higher HF bands (20-10m).

Trying to get one antenna that will work well on all of the MF and HF bands is *very* difficult.

The ZS6BKW variant

Brian Austin, ZS6BKW/G0GSF, spent some time trying to optimise the G5RV. He found that by reducing the overall length to 93ft and extending the matching section to 39.8ft (12.13m) of 450-ohm ladderline (VF=0.9) it would provide a reasonable match on five bands. The antenna would be usable on all of 40m, 17m and 12m without any tuner, and much of 20m and 10m. It still needs a tuner to cover the popular 80m and 15m bands though.

So if you are limited for space, the ZS6BKW could be made from scratch, or from a cannibalised G5RV, and give you a reasonable all-round antenna for very little money.

W5GI Mystery Antenna

W5GI's 'Mystery Antenna' gets a lot of attention. It looks a little like a G5RV, but inventor John Basilotto, W5GI included coaxial stubs to produce what he called 'a coaxial colinear array on 20m'.

It consists of a half wavelength (at 20m) of 300-ohm ribbon that feeds a dipole centre. Either side of the dipole centre are two pieces of wire 16ft 6in long. These are then each connected to the inner of a 16ft 6in piece of RG58 coax. The outer is left unconnected. The far end of this is then shorted and connected to a further 16ft 6in of wire, giving an antenna with a total span of around 100ft (including insulators and the feed point).

The main constructional difficulties are encountered in making sure the joins are strong enough to support the weight and tension (there are many reports of breakages). It is best to use heatshrink tubing on the joints, to waterproof them.

I used standard 300-ohm windowed ribbon feeder and a half wavelength came out at 8.3m (27ft 3in).

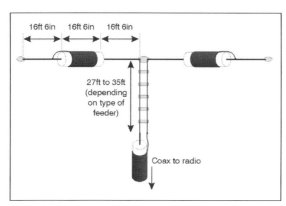

16ft 6in   16ft 6in   16ft 6in

27ft to 35ft (depending on type of feeder)

Coax to radio

The W5GI 'Mystery Antenna' has been found to give a decent performance on 3.5MHz and 7MHz.

Getting Started in Amateur Radio

The 'mystery' part of the name refers to the fact that it is supposed to be almost impossible to computer model the antenna, as it uses coaxial stubs. What we can say is that W5GI said that the stubs caused the antenna to feed the three radiating elements in phase, although all the evidence points to the fact that the antenna does *not* have three in-phase elements on 20m.

The real questions are; Does the antenna work? And is it worth making?

In my local club (Norfolk Amateur Radio Club) we have built quite a few W5GI antennas. What we have found is that it works well on 3.5MHz (80m) and 7MHz (40m), and is not bad on 14MHz (20m) either, but it is not a very good performer on the higher bands and on 30m (10MHz) it is not a good match.

I used the W5GI antenna for the 2014 RSGB 80m Club Championships and people often remarked how loud I was, despite the antenna lying on the apex of the roof. I beat my own personal best score on CW one week, so it was working!

It also seems useful for 40m (7MHz), giving a relatively easy match and good performance. I have broken pile-ups into Europe with it on 40m.

We have also used a W5GI dipole for our club's entry into the International Marconi Day event at Caister Lifeboat on the Norfolk Coast and each year we generate big pile-ups with it on 40m.

Once you climb past 40m though it become a little more unpredictable, whch can be a characteristic of 'long' antennas, where their multi-lobe pattern either works for or against you.

In conclusion, I'm not sure the antenna works any better than a G5RV. In fact, if you are looking for an antenna of roughly the same length, with similar performance, but with a better match, check-out the ZS6BKW variant mentioned earlier.

A simple and cheap vertical antenna for 28MHz

Vertical antennas can be quite useful. They take up very little space and have a low angle of radiation, which is useful for DXing. One downside though is that verticals can be a little more noisy on receive than horizontal antennas, although this depends on location.

The antenna described here is a Resonant Feedline Dipole (RFD). It has been mentioned in various magazines, but was probably first described by W2OZH in the August 1991 issue of *QST* magazine in the USA.

To make one you take a length of coaxial cable, such as RG58, and at one end attach a quarter wavelength of wire to the cable's centre conductor. You don't actually connect the cable's shield to anything at this point.

You then go a quarter-wave down the coaxial cable and make an RF choke, by winding the coax cable into a coil. The antenna is then a vertical half-wave dipole, comprising a quarter-wave wire, with the other quarter-wave using the outer of the coaxial cable. This can be suspended in the air from a tree branch or taped to a fibreglass fishing pole, with the remainder of the coax run to your transceiver.

The RFD takes advantage of the fact that coaxial cable acts like a three conductor cable for RF. There is the inner conductor, the inside of the shield, and the outside of the shield. When we transmit, RF signals travel down the inside of the cable.

When the current gets to the point where the quarter-wave wire is connected to the inner of the coax, the current on the inner conductor continues right on up the quarter-wave wire. The current on the inside of the shield now goes back down the outside of the shield. We want it to stop after going a quarter of a wavelength and to do that we put a high impedance choke in its path, by winding the coax into a coil. This does not affect the signal on the inside of the cable, but it stops the current flow on the outside of the shield.

The big benefit of the RFD is that it is end fed, which makes it convenient to install. It also gives a low SWR on its design frequency, so you don't need to use a tuner.

So that's the theory, but what about how it works out in reality? A quarter wavelength of wire cut for 28.5MHz should be 2.63m long. In reality though, if we are using PVC-coated wire (which has a lower velocity factor), you should actually cut it at about 2.5m. You may find that you need to fold it over a little to bring the low SWR point to where you want it in the 10m band once it is installed, but don't do that yet.

We then solder the quarter wavelength of wire to the inner conductor of the coax, leaving the outer braid connected to nothing.

Next we measure 2.5m down the coax and start to create our choke. At this point get hold of a cylinder with a diameter of about about 4.25 inches (112 mm). I used a plastic container that I found in the kitchen. Now lay some pre-cut 8in strips of gaffer or duct tape on the container, with the adhesive side pointing outwards. Now start winding your choke onto the former, keeping it nice and neat ,with no spaces between the turns. In total you need five turns, then you can tape the whole thing neatly together using the gaffer tape.

If you want to know more about how to make high impedance chokes and see the results of Steve, G3TXQ's experiments, look on the Internet at: at www.karinya.net/g3txq/chokes/

Once you have the choke completed it is relatively simple to tune the antenna, Either hang it from a tree branch (keeping it away from metal objects) or tape it to a fibreglass fishing pole. I use a metal washing line ground spike to mount my fishing pole.

To tune the antenna, measure the SWR using your radio. Alternatively, an antenna analyser at the frequency you are interested in. If you find the SWR is better at a lower frequency, the antenna is too long. Don't cut the top wire, just fold it over on itself by a couple of inches and secure it with PVC insulation tape, then take the SWR reading again.

You should be able to get the SWR down to below 1.5:1 at your frequency of operation – around 28.5MHz if you like SSB, 28.1MHz if you prefer CW (Morse), or 29.6MHz if you want to operate FM.

2.5m

2.5m

Coax choke

Coax to radio

This cheap and cheerful vertical antenna for 10m works remarkably well.

A simple multiband vertical for HF

As we've shown it is reasonably easy to build a simple monoband vertical antenna for one HF band. Making a multiband antenna is a little more difficult.

The usual method is to use traps, which can be tricky to build or expensive to buy, but there is another antenna that will let you work at least five bands, possibly more, and it doesn't cost a fortune to make either.

Getting Started in Amateur Radio

The antenna is called a 'Rybakov' and is featured in my book *Stealth Antennas*, the second edition of which has just been published.

The Rybakov is so called because it uses a fibreglass fishing pole – 'rybakov' meaning 'fisherman' or 'family of a fishermen' in Russian.

The antenna is a 7.6m vertical, fed with a 4:1 Un-Un (unbalanced to unbalanced transformer) as described by IV3SBE. You can see the full constructional details at http://www.iv3sbe.webfundis.net/html/Rybakov806.htm

The antenna works reasonably well when supported with a fibreglass fishing pole and can be put up in a few minutes.

The idea is that the antenna represents a non-1:1 SWR match at all frequencies from 40m (7MHz) to 10m (28MHz).

The length of 7.6m was chosen because it isn't a half wave (high impedance) or quarter wave (low impedance) on any amateur band. A 4:1 Un-Un (unbalanced to unbalanced transformer) transforms the impedance to something closer to 1:1, thereby reducing losses in the coax.

You will also need to put down an earth stake at the base of the antenna and it really, really needs radials – the more the merrier. You should find the SWR figure at the radio to be less than 6:1 on all bands, with many bands being less than 3:1. You will need to use an antenna tuning unit (ATU).

The radiation pattern on 30m (10MHz) and 20m (14MHz) is typical of a vertical and good for DX. It is not as good on the higher bands, because the antenna is longer than a quarter wave and the radiation pattern becomes complex. If you extend the wire to 8.6m in length it will be better on 40m (7MHz). It still won't be ideal for contacts around the UK on 40m, as the radiation pattern will be wrong. Ideally you should use a low-ish horizontal antenna with a large skyward lobe for this. For 20m-10m (14-28MHz) use you are better sticking to 7.6m.

Antenna modelling shows that radials are critical for this antenna and you may get different SWR readings, depending on how many you have. A single earth stake might give you a low SWR, but the antenna will be lossy. More radials might help – just make sure they are roughly the same length as the radiating element and aim for as many as possible (16+ is good).

If you try this antenna with just a ground stake you may be disappointed, but as a cheap, compromise HF antenna the Rybakov works quite well.

The Rybakov vertical is another cheap and simple antenna that will work on a number of HF bands, although you will need to use an ATU.

Making a 2m Slim Jim antenna with 300-ohm ribbon cable

The chances are, if you are newly licensed, you will want to operate on the 2m band (145MHz). After all, there are plenty of people to talk to, lots of repeaters, and the antennas are quite small. You will also find local nets on the band and even the RSGB's GB2RS

News service. You could go and buy an antenna for the band, but why not make your own?

A very easy antenna to make, which will work well, is the Slim Jim. It was designed originally by the late Fred Judd, G2BCX. The 'Jim' stands for 'J impedance matched', which describes how the antenna works. I have made these before and they work well.

Cut a piece of white, translucent 300-ohm ribbon cable 60inches/1.52m long and bare the wires at both ends by about half an inch. Next, twist the ends together and solder them, giving you an overall length of 59inches/ 1.5m. Then cut a one-inch/25.4mm slot on one side, about 18inches/0.46m up from the bottom. Connect your 50-ohm coax (RG58 or RG213) across the two wire elements about 2inches/50mm from the bottom. Fit a PL259 or other suitable plug to the other end of the coaxial cable.

This should result in an SWR of about 1.1-1.5 :1 at 145MHz. If you have no way of measuring the SWR it might be an idea to get a fellow ham to test it for you.

The finished Slim Jim can now be put in a piece of white PVC tubing from the local hardware store. I finished mine off with the silver top off a spray can on one end and the end off a toothpaste tube on the other, with the coax coming out of a hole in the bottom. I just glued them on, making sure that all the joints were waterproofed. It looked quite good and cost about £5 all in.

Once you have made the antenna you need to mount it vertically, as high as you can. In a high tree branch, on the chimney or even hanging in the loft from the apex of the rafters. It will work in all of these places, but outside and in the clear is usually better. The antenna will give you good low-angle radiation on 2m, just right for working FM simplex and via repeaters. And if people ask, you can say that you made the antenna yourself.

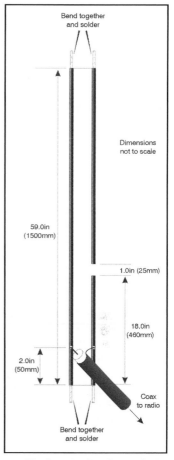

Made out of a piece of 300 Ohm ribbon feeder, this 'Slim Jim' antenna will outperform any 'rubber duck' on a 2m handheld transceiver.

An added bonus is that it will also work reasonably well *on receive* for the marine (156-162MHz) and aeronautical bands (108-137MHz).

Conclusion

There are hundreds of different antenna designs that you can build – you don't need to buy one. However, if you are not mechanically minded and would rather purchase something ready made, talk to a few amateurs before you part with your hard-earned cash.

Some commercial designs work better than others and it is obviously better to find out which they are before you buy anything. If you don't know any other amateurs, there are local clubs to join also a lot of technical reviews to read at www.eham.net.

Chapter 7.
Basic FM and SSB operating

Making your first QSO

Your first contact or conversation (QSO) can be quite daunting. For this reason it might be a good idea to arrange a contact with a friend or someone else in your radio club.

In that way it will be less stressful and if you make a hash of it it won't really matter. Also, it might be better to arrange the QSO to take place on 2m FM, rather than HF SSB, because HF will be noisier and more prone to interference.

If you are not familiar with the terms FM and SSB, FM stands for Frequency Modulation. It gives the crystal clear audio you may be accustomed to from a broadcast radio station on your car radio, but as the signal declines it suddenly gets noisy until all you are left with is hiss. This is why you have a 'squelch' control – to block-off the audio when there is no signal present.

SSB stands for Single SideBand. It is a very efficient mode that is generally used on HF, although it is also used on VHF and UHF.

At first, you may find it difficult to tune an SSB signal in. Get it wrong and the person on the other end can sound like Donald Duck! When operating SSB you can select to hear either the Upper SideBand (USB) or Lower SideBand (LSB). Radio amateurs traditionally use LSB on 160m (1.8MHz), 80m (3.5MHz) and 40m (7MHz). Upper sideband is used on 20m (14MHz) and above.

If you select the wrong sideband signals will be garbled – you won't be able to understand what people are talking about!

The first thing to do is make sure your radio is set up properly – that it is on the right mode (FM, USB or LSB), with the microphone gain set correctly

Make sure you have selected the correct mode. Here I have selected FM on 2m (145MHz).

and you have selected the right amount of power. Generally we should use the minimum amount of power required to guarantee a good contact.

Then you need to make sure that you are using the correct antenna and that it is matched properly, either by using an antenna tuning unit (ATU), if you are on HF, or by feeding it directly. If feeding it directly, such as you might with a dipole cut for the band you are operating on, make sure that it presents a low SWR to your radio – that is, that you installed it correctly and it is working fine.

If you are on HF and using a manual ATU you will need to find the right combination of inductance and capacitance to make sure your radio sees a low SWR (lower than 2:1) on the band you wish to operate. Once you have found the best combination make a note of the settings so that you can use them again when you are next on that band.

Some radios have a built-in ATU. If so it is just a case of reducing the power output and pressing a button until the internal ATU finds a match. You can then increase the power again before transmitting.

Don't worry if this is all gobbledegook, because the ATU tuning procedure is looked at when you take the practical assessment of your Foundation exam.

To conduct a voice or phone QSO you now have two choices: You can call 'CQ' or you can answer someone who is calling CQ. A CQ ('seek you') is simply a general call to no one in particular. It is the traditional way of seeking random contacts.

Before calling CQ it's important to find a frequency that is not occupied by any other station. This may not be easy, particularly in crowded band conditions on HF.

If you are on VHF FM a good starting point is the calling frequency on 145.500MHz.

Always listen before transmitting. Make sure the frequency isn't being used before you go barging in. If, after a reasonable time, the frequency seems clear, ask 'Is this frequency in use?', followed by your callsign. If nobody replies, you're clear to call.

When you first start, have a few ideas of what you might talk about jotted down on a pad.

Now call CQ using the 'three x three' method. So it is: "CQ CQ CQ this is Mike Six Alpha Bravo Charlie, Mike Six Alpha Bravo Charlie, Mike Six Alpha Bravo Charlie standing by."

Later we'll look at the phonetic alphabet, which is what we use to make sure people don't mistake one letter of our callsign for another.

If a station comes back to you say: "M1ABC (or whatever) this is Mike Six Alpha Bravo Charlie. Good evening/day, your report is 59 (or whatever it is), my name is (for example) Dave – Delta Alpha Victor Echo – and my QTH is <where you live> London – Lima Oscar November Delta Oscar November."

Note that you don't usually need to spell things out phonetically more than once.

If lucky, they should come back to you with your report, their name and QTH.

Getting Started in Amateur Radio

At this point you have two choices – you can go on to give them a few more details about your station, such as the radio, power and antenna, but with many QSOs on HF you may find that the other station wishes you 73 and wants to go. This usually means that English is not their first language and they are likely to get tongue tied.

If they do speak good English you can always tell them a little about yourself and your local area, and ask them about theirs. Or you could tell them what clubs you are a member of. There are a whole host of topics you can discuss. Discussions on politics and religion tend to attract controversy and start arguments on the air, so if it looks like your conversation is heading in one of those directions it might be a good idea to finish the QSO.

Conduct yourself as though anyone in the world might be listening at any time – because the likelihood is that a lot of people are. Whenever you transmit, you're representing all of the amateur radio community and your country, so act accordingly.

At the end of the QSO wish the other station '73' – which is the amateur radio code for 'best wishes' – and say you are now going QRT (closing down).

There – that wasn't so bad, was it?

Using the NATO phonetic alphabet

One of the things you learn as part of your foundation licence is the NATO phonetic alphabet. This is an important tool for amateurs and helps no end when discussing your details with someone who doesn't have English as their first language.

When using SSB or even FM, if you need to spell out your callsign or another word it pays to use the phonetic alphabet, otherwise you can get confusion between some letters, such as 'S' and 'F', or 'P' and 'B'.

For example, if your callsign is M6BPF, then phonetically you might say 'This is M6BPF – Mike Six Bravo Papa Foxtrot'. This will save a lot of misunderstanding.

You can also use it to spell out your address or QTH. For example, if you live in Leeds, you might say 'My QTH is Leeds – Lima Echo Echo Delta Sierra'.

We will have a look at Q codes shortly.

History of the phonetic alphabet and other terms

Where did the phonetic alphabet come from? And is there more to it than meets the eye?

The NATO phonetic alphabet is more accurately known as the International Radiotelephony Spelling Alphabet. It is also called the ICAO (International Civil Aviation Organisation) phonetic or ICAO spelling alphabet, and the ITU phonetic alphabet.

The ICAO developed this system in the 1950s, in order to account for discrepancies that might arise in communications as a result of multiple alphabet naming systems coexisting in different places

A	Alpha
B	Bravo
C	Charlie
D	Delta
E	Echo
F	Foxtrot
G	Golf
H	Hotel
I	India
J	Juliet
K	Kilo
L	Lima
M	Mike
N	November
O	Oscar
P	Papa
Q	Quebec
R	Romeo
S	Sierra
T	Tango
U	Uniform
V	Victor
W	Whiskey
X	X-ray
Y	Yankee
Z	Zulu

The phonetic alphabet.

and organisations.

In the official version of the alphabet, the non-English spellings Alfa and Juliett are used. Alfa is spelled with an 'f' as it is in most European languages, because the English and French spelling 'alpha' would not be pronounced properly by native speakers of some other languages – who may not know that 'ph' should be pronounced as 'f'.

Juliett is spelled with a 'tt' for French speakers, because they may otherwise treat a single final 't' as silent. In some English versions of the alphabet, one or both of these may have their standard English spelling.

Did you know that some of the 26 words have altered pronunciations too? Charlie can be either 'char-lee' or 'shar-lee', and Uniform is either 'you-nee-form' or 'oo-nee-form', which is not the English pronunciation of the word.

Oscar is pronounced 'oss-cah' and Victor as 'vik-tah' without the 'r', even by people who would normally pronounce it. Papa is pronounced 'Pa-PAH', with the accent on the second syllable instead of the first.

The code word Quebec is often pronounced as the French 'keh-beck'.

The final choice of code words for the letters of the alphabet and for the digits was made after hundreds of thousands of comprehension tests involving 31 nationalities. The qualifying feature was the likelihood of a code word being understood in the context of others. For example, 'football' has a higher chance of being understood than 'foxtrot' in isolation, but foxtrot is superior in extended communication.

And finally, although not specifically related to the phonetic alphabet, it is interesting to look at the origins of a few more words we use in radio.

For example, 'mayday' is based on the French 'm'aidez', meaning 'help me'. Many other words used in marine radio have French origins, such as 'sécurité, sécurité, sécurité', which means that what follows is important safety information.

Or 'pan, pan, pan-pan', which informs potential rescuers (including emergency services and other craft in the area) that a safety problem exists. It comes from the French word 'panne', which means a mechanical failure or breakdown of some kind.

And finally, what about 'CQ'? A French friend of mine thought it might stand for 'Cherche Quelqu'un' - literally the French for 'looking for someone', but G3HAL says that according to Wikipedia, land telegraphs traditionally used 'CQ' ('sécu', from the French word sécurité) to identify alert or precautionary messages of interest to all stations along a telegraph line.

That is probably the best explanation.

Using Q codes

The international Q code is an abbreviated way to exchange information with a a simple code. It consists of three-letter groups, with each group having a specific meaning and each group beginning with the letter Q.

Q codes also helps amateurs understand each other, even if they have limited foreign language skills. For example, if you want to say 'My location is London', you can say 'My QTH is London' instead. Most radio amateurs in whatever country they live would recognise 'QTH' as being location or address. Likewise they would recognise 'QSB' as fading or more specifically 'The strength of your signals varies'.

Q codes can be used as statements or questions. This is more relevant to Morse

QRM	Are you being interfered with? / I am being interfered with.
QRN	Are you troubled by static? / I am troubled by static.
QRT	Must I stop transmission? / Stop transmission.
QRV	Are you ready? / I am ready.
QRX	When will you call again? / I will call you again at ... hours (on ... kHz).
QRZ	By whom am I being called? / You are being called by ...
QSB	Does the strength of my signals vary? / The strength of your signals varies.
QSL	Can you acknowledge receipt? / I am acknowledging receipt.
QSY	Shall I change to ... kilohertz ? / Change to ... kilohertz
QTH	What is your position (location)? / My position (location) is ....

Common Q codes.

code, where Q codes play a very important role.

Can you imagine have to send 'My location is London' every QSO? Just sending 'QTH London' gets the same amount of information through in far fewer letters. And instead of sending "What is your location?" you can just send 'QTH?'.

Chapter 8.
CW and digital modes

Introduction

Most people think of amateur radio as being two people just talking to each other with microphones, but the hobby is much broader than that.

Amateur radio's roots started with Continuous Wave (CW) using Morse code. For many amateurs CW remains their only mode, for the reasons we are about to explain; but computers have opened-up a lot more opportunities for digital communications, with a whole host of keyboard-to-keyboard modes that appeal to digitally-minded people and work well with low power, such as the 10 watts used by amateurs with a Foundation licence.

So let's take a closer look.

Morse Code (CW)

Many would-be radio amateurs were put off by the fact that they thought they had to learn Morse code, but UK radio amateurs haven't had to do that to obtain their licence since July 2003.

Prior to that date the International Telecommunication Union (ITU) required an assessment of Morse code proficiency to be part of the global amateur

Morse code (CW) can be sent via a straight key or a paddle.

radio licensing procedure, but since then Morse code has become an optional element in amateur radio practice and many countries have now removed the compulsory Morse component from their amateur radio licence requirements.

So does that mean that Morse is dead? Far from it! You only have to listen to the bottom end of most of the HF bands - such as 40m (7MHz) or 20m (14MHz) - to realise that far from being dead, Morse code is alive, well and being used by increasing numbers of hams.

The answer as to why is simple. Morse code gets through when SSB fails miserably. This isn't just the die-hard CW fans speaking, it is a well-known, demonstrable fact. A CW signal can have more than a 10-20dB advantage over a SSB signal.

Hams around the world work distant, rare countries every day using CW and 100W or less, plus basic wire antennas, when single sideband (SSB) signals from those parts of the world are virtually inaudible.

An SSB signal usually occupies about 2.5KHz. An FM signal will take up about 10KHz, but a CW QSO can take place in a bandwidth of about 300Hz. If you are only listening to a single tone in a narrow bandwidth it is a lot easier to filter out QRM and electrical interference. This is very important in urban areas and with compromise antennas, which are more prone to picking up noise from nearby electrical wiring, domestic TVs, power line transmission (PLT) and a host of other pieces of equipment.

Most DXpeditions put a lot of emphasis on CW as an operating mode. While it may be possible to work them on SSB, Morse code is often easier.

So what other reasons could you have for learning CW?

Repeaters identify themselves with Morse code, so if you learn it you will be able to find out what you listening to and what CTCSS (Continuous Tone-Coded Squelch System) code you need to access them. And beacons also use Morse to identify themselves. By listening to them you can find out what countries you can hear on the 10m band (from around 28.150-28.400MHz).

Simple CW transmitters can also be made quite easily (SSB transceivers are usually more complex) and as CW is more effi-

You can even get a touch keyer that requires a very light touch to send Morse.

cient than SSB, AM or FM you can often get away with less effective antennas or lower power levels to make your contacts. This means you are less likely to cause interference and you can still work DX with 'stealthy' antennas, even though your Foundation licence limits you to 10 Watts. CW involves no accent or pronunciation problems, and is a widely-understood international language.

So how do you go about learning Morse code? The secret is to do it properly, and that is where both your local club and/or the GB2RS Morse code broadcasts come in very useful. If you are just starting out we recommend that you read G3LDI's book *Morse Code for Radio Amateurs*, which is available from the RSGB book shop.

Radio teletype (RTTY) – keyboard to keyboard communications

If you listen to the HF bands you may have come across the distinctive 'trill' of RTTY or radioteletype.

This is two radio amateurs communicating via their keyboards – sending text to each other in real-time over the airwaves, a bit like a text chat but where you get to see every letter being keyed. They are also using the amateur bands instead of the Internet or a mobile phone.

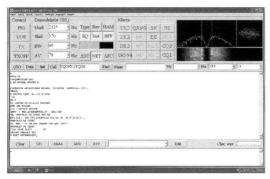

RTTY software is mostly free. This is MMTTY in action.

RTTY is a Baudot code that is transmitted using two different audio tones – called 'mark' and 'space'. It is the combination of these two tones (which are distinctive, as one is higher than the other) that form the different letters and numbers that we can receive.

On the amateur HF bands we use five-bit Baudot, meaning that every character consists of five bits, either mark or space. To this we add a start bit and two stop bits.

In general, a baud rate or speed of 45.45 baud is used on HF, which is the equivalent of about 60 words per minute. Even though 45.45 is standard, you will occasionally come across a RTTY signal at a different speed – 75 baud (100 wpm).

The standard mark and space tones are 2125Hz and 2295Hz respectively, which are 170Hz apart. For this reason you often hear amateur RTTY described as '45.5/170'.

The biggest decision you will need to make when you begin to set up for RTTY is whether you want to use AFSK (audio frequency shift keying) or FSK (frequency shift keying) to transmit. With AFSK your sound card or other interface generates the audio tones, which are then fed into your rig's mic or audio input. With FSK a special interface tells the rig to transmit the right frequencies (on SSB), to give the same effect.

Both work well, although AFSK is perhaps more suited to beginners as it works with most sound cards and computers. RTTY purists often move on to dedicated terminals or interfaces that can control FSK signals.

```
OUOPOLIO DE I2DKJ

SOFTWARE : DM780 V5.24.0.36 RELEASE
QTH : HR MILANO
LOC : JN45PM JN45PM
INFO : WWW.ARICERNUSCO.IT ; QRZ.COM
OM, OUOPOLIO DE I2DKJ PSE KN

OUOPOLIO DE I2DKJ
OK  MSG - 73 OM AND THANKS FOR QSO  RTTY.
OUOPOLIO DE I2DKJ
CIAO FROM ITALY ...    SK

-------------------------------------------

ON4LCX DE 9A3UJ

ALL  COPIED TNX FER INFO
DR MICHEL  GL GD DX HPE CU AGN
GOOD LUCK TO YOU AND YOUR FAMILY.
MY QSL IS FINE VIA BURO. LOTW AND EQSL.CC,

MNI TNX FOR THE QSO , BEST DX AND 73 FROM CROATIA
ON4LCX DE 9A3UJ BYE  BYE 73 TU SK

-------------------------------------------

R95RGA DE SP2AEK GOOD AFTERNOON DR OM  UR RSQ IS 599  MY
NAME IS ROMAN
ROMAN AND QTH BYDGOSZCZ BYDGOSZCZ HW?

DR OM    R95RGA DE SP2AEK KN G
... ROMAN
BE BYE 73
```

This is the sort of information that is passed during a typical RTTY QSO.

Most modern transceivers today have an FSK input and by using the FSK input to your transceiver, you can then operate the radio in the RTTY or FSK position and make use of filters available for reception, such as a narrow 250Hz or 500Hz IF filter. In most cases, when using AFSK, your radio will be placed in the LSB position and you will have to use the filters you normally have access to when in LSB. This may well include narrow DSP (Digital Signal Processing) filters if you have a modern radio.

When operating AFSK, you must make sure the audio coming from your TNC or sound card is at the correct level. If it is too high it will overdrive your transmitter and more than likely result in a distorted signal, or it might put out an 'image' signal across the band. In general, make sure that you don't see any reading when you switch your meter to ALC. You must also make sure you do

Contests (common)	USA (common)	USA (DX)	Europe/Africa (common)	Japan (common)
1800-1810 /1835-1845	1800-1810	1838-1843	1838-1843	
3570-3600	3580 - 3600	3590	3580-3620	3520-3530
7025-7100	7025-7050 /7080-7100	7040	7035-7045	7025-7040
	10120-10150		10140-10150	
14060-14120	14080-14100		14080-14100	
	18100-18110		18100-18110	
21060-21150	21080-21100		21080-21120	
	24910-24930		24920-24930	
28060-28150	28080-28100		28050-28150	

Common RTTY frequencies (in kHz).

not have the speech processor turned on when transmitting AFSK RTTY.

For beginners, we'll concentrate on AFSK for now.

So what do you need in terms of equipment?

Firstly you will need an HF transceiver capable of receiving/transmitting SSB signals, plus an antenna. Next you will need a computer. There are RTTY programs available for Linux and Mac computers, but the bulk are available for PCs running Windows.

Next you will need an interface, to connect your computer to the radio. You can make one of these yourself, or you can buy one, generally for less than £100. It is important that you use a proper interface, as they can prevent ground loops that can damage a transceiver, plus they can prevent hums and other interference.

You will also need a computer program, such as MixW, MMTTY, Digital Master 780 or something similar.

Once set up, go to a known RTTY area, such as 14.080 - 14.099MHz (avoid the beacons at 14.100MHz), plug in your interface and cables, run your software and see if you can tune the signal in to decode the RTTY signals. You'll find that the tuning needs to be quite precise.

Before you transmit, it might be a good idea to read more about RTTY, to make sure you're a "'good citizen' in terms of your operating procedure. A good starting point is G3LDI's book *RTTY/PSK31 for Radio Amateurs*, which is available from the RSGB bookshop.

There is also a free nine-page 'Getting Started with RTTY' document available to download at www.bartg.org.uk.

PSK31

PSK31 is another highly-efficient data mode that lets you work long distances, even when you can barely hear the signal. PSK31 stands for Phase Shift Keying 31 baud (or 31 bits per second – bps).

Unlike RTTY (radio teletype) the characters are formed by changing the phase of the sound wave, not by using different tones. A PSK31 signal just sounds like a single tone or note, but with a slight wobble. It is used for real-time keyboard-to-keyboard informal text 'chats' over the air.

The other main difference between RTTY and PSK31 is that with PSK31 you have access to both upper (capitals) and lower case letters. It works very well at low power levels and for this reason has become a firm favourite for QRP and stealth antenna operators.

PSK31 was developed by Peter Martinez, G3PLX and introduced to the amateur radio community in late 1998. The mode was enthusiastically received and has since spread quickly into worldwide use. It can often overcome interference and poor propagation conditions in situations where voice or other data methods of communication fail.

Contacts can be conducted at less than 100Hz separation, so with disciplined operation at least 20 simultaneous PSK31 contacts can be carried out side-by-side in the bandwidth required for just one SSB voice contact. Typically you can make good round-the-world PSK31 contacts with 10-25W.

So what do you need to operate PSK31? First, you need a transceiver capable of working on single side band (SSB). You'll actually be using upper sideband (USB). Next you will need some software, such as FLDIGI, Digipan or WinPSK. Most of the packages are free. Lastly you'll need a data interface and cables to connect your computer (Windows, Mac or Linux) to your transceiver. You can build your own or buy one ready made. The signals from your computer are fed via the interface to either the radio's microphone

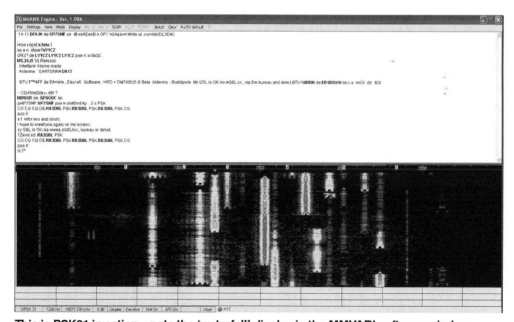

This is PSK31 in action – note the 'waterfall' display in the MMVARI software window.

jack or an auxiliary connection into the transceiver, where they are transmitted. This can be the same interface that you use for RTTY.

The best way to get started is set the system up and see if you can decode some of the PSK31 signals on, say, 14.070MHz (20m). Before you transmit you will need to make sure that you are not overdriving your transceiver. There is a good guide to using PSK31 at www.podxs070.com.

There are a few downsides to PSK31. One is that many contacts tend to be 'rubber stamp', with amateurs just sending pre-prepared texts or macros. Some of these leave a lot to be desired, as many operators seem to think that you might be interested in what sound card and other computer equipment they are using.

If you are a DX chaser the other limitation is that many DXpeditions don't operate much (if any) PSK31. For DXing you might be better off adding CW to your arsenal of skills, but if you are limited in terms of what antennas you can put up PSK31 will let you make guaranteed contacts when SSB could be virtually impossible.

Amateur Band	USB Dial Frequency
160m	1838.150kHz
80m	3580.150kHz
40m (Europe)	7035.150kHz
30m	10142.150kHz
20m	14070.150kHz
17m	18100.150kHz
15m	21080.150kHz
12m	24920.150kHz
10m	28120.150kHz

HF PSK31 frequencies.

WSPR

Did you know that there is another mode that will let you both receive and transmit signals from right around the world, with less than 10 watts of power?

WSPR (pronounced 'whisper') stands for 'Weak Signal Propagation Reporter'. It uses a computer program to send and receive and is used for weak-signal radio communication between amateurs.

The program was initially written by Nobel prizewinning physicist Joe Taylor, K1JT, and it is designed for sending and receiving low-power transmissions to test propagation paths on the MF and HF bands.

WSPR stations use low power transmissions – typically just a few watts. First released in April 2008, WSPR uses a transmission mode called MEPT-JT - the MEPT standing for Manned Experimental Propagation Transmitter, 'JT' for Joe Taylor.

WSPR isn't a two-way communication mode as such, in that you don't hold conventional QSOs, but the principle is quite simple. Stations running WSPR automatically transmit a beacon signal on a given frequency. Each transmission lasts for just under two minutes and to make sure this all works you must ensure that your computer clock is set correctly, or you will clash. Receiving stations around the world listen for your signal and, if it is heard, send the results via the Internet to http://wsprnet.org/.

When your system is not transmitting it listens for these WSPR beacon signals as well. If it hears one, it logs it and sends the details via the Internet to WSPRnet, which then logs your information and displays it on a map, along with the others.

To receive WSPR you need to connect your radio's audio output to the Microphone or Line In socket of your computer. If you want to transmit as well you will need to connect the speaker output of the computer to the radio and also arrange for it to be

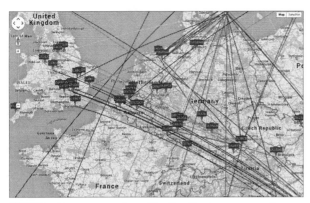

WSPRnet.org can automatically display a map of where you are being received in the world.

keyed. If you have an interface for data modes you are almost there, as the principle is just like RTTY or PSK31.

WSPR signals have a barely discernible warble to them, but carry your callsign, your Locator and your power output. It actually uses Frequency Shift Keying with a very small shift, occupying a bandwidth of about 6Hz. This means that many stations can be fitted into the 200Hz WSPR window.

WSPRnet will not only tell you who heard you (usually within a minute or two), but also the received signal to noise ratio, the distance and bearing between your two stations. The end result is quite fascinating, as it gives you an at-a-glance view of real-time propagation. It is perfectly possible to find your 5W signals being received in Hawaii or Australia.

Before you rush out to get started on WSPR it is worth pointing out that there are a few pitfalls you need to be careful of, including making sure you have selected the correct band in the software, that you have set your power output correctly in dBm and that you are not overdriving the transmitter.

For those who are interested in finding out more about WSPR I suggest you read the excellent article by Julian, G4ILO (sadly now silent key) at www.g4ilo.com/wspr.html. This gives you a good run through of what WSPR is about and how to set it up.

You can also download the free WSPR software and quick start guide at
www.physics.princeton.edu/pulsar/K1JT/

Band	Dial Freq (USB)
160	1.8366MHz
80m	3.5926MHz
40m	7.0386MHz
30m	10.1387MHz
20m	14.0956MHz
17m	18.1046MHz
15m	21.0946MHz
12m	24.9246MHz
10m	28.1246MHz
6m	50.293MHz
2m	144.4885MHz

WSPR Frequencies.

Weak signal work with JT modes

There is another mode that is particularly suited to two-way communication with low power and poor signals. It is called JT65 and it enables you to pull DX signals out of the noise on HF. With a just a couple of watts you could make a confirmed two-way contact with another radio amateur in Australia or New Zealand.

Like WSPR, JT65 was invented by Joe Taylor, K1JT, a professor emeritus of physics at Princeton University. Joe actually shares a Nobel Prize in astrophysics and the amateur community counts itself lucky that he is one of us!

There are many variants of JT65, which Joe originally designed to optimize EME (Earth-Moon-Earth) contacts on the HF and VHF bands. The one you might be interested in for HF is JT65A, which is actually a sub-mode of Joe's original JT65 protocol.

Getting Started in Amateur Radio

JT65 includes advanced error-correcting features that make it very robust, even with signals that are too weak to be heard by ear. It is too complex to explain how to set it up here, other than to say that you need to install the software and connect your computer to your radio, much as you do with WSPR and PSK31.

If you are interested in finding out more I suggest you Google JT65 and take a look at some of the excellent tutorials and videos that explain the mode and its uses.

Analogue SSTV

Tune your HF transceiver around 14.230MHz USB and sooner or later you will hear a strange tick-tock musical sound. This is Slow Scan TV, or SSTV for short. SSTV is a way of sending still images around the world. They are in full colour, although with analogue SSTV the quality is not always perfect. It will depend on the quality of the signal.

So what do you need to receive and send SSTV images? Firstly, a stable HF transceiver or receiver capable of receiving HF SSB signals. You will also need a computer to decode them – SSTV software packages are available for Windows and Mac OSX machines, as well as Linux.

You will also need a way of interfacing your radio and your computer. The easiest way is to buy an interface with the right cables for your radio. One again this will be the same type of interface you would use for RTTY or PSK31 transmission and reception.

If you just want to sample what SSTV reception is like, you could even take a low-level audio output from your radio and feed it into the microphone socket of your computer.

There are a whole host of different SSTV packages available. Some are paid for, while others are free. One of the most popular free packages is MMSSTV by Mako JE3HHT. You can download it at http://hamsoft.ca/pages/mmsstv.php

Once you have installed the MMSSTV software and connected your computer to your radio, with it tuned to 14.230MHz you are ready to start. If you run MMSSTV it will automatically start decoding SSTV images. All you have to do is make sure you are tuned in correctly to the the signal and that the correct mode has been selected. In the middle of the screen you will see a vertical bar with 'RX Mode' at the top. Just make sure you select 'Auto'.

To tune the radio you need to keep and eye on the MMSSTV tuning indicator towards the right of the display and aim to keep the signal within the vertical

SSTV images received on 20m (14MHz) from an Italian station.

1200 and 2300Hz bars. This will make more sense when you see it.

As MMSSTV receives images it will automatically store them in the frames at the bottom of the screen. Other frequencies where SSTV transmissions take place are 3.730MHz, 7.171MHz, 21.340MHz and 28.680MHz.

MMSSTV also lets you design your own SSTV images for transmission, or you can import images and add your own callsign details. It is probably best to practice with receiving images before you try transmitting them.

A word of warning! SSTV is a 100% duty cycle mode so you must turn the power output of your transceiver down to about 25-50W when transmitting, to stop it overheating.

Finally, there is also a high quality digital SSTV mode that requires different software, which is what we are going to look at next.

Digital SSTV

Recent years have seen the introduction of a whole new method of sending images across the airwaves – digital SSTV.

In fact, the term 'slow scan' shouldn't be used at all, as it is really a file transfer, also known as DRM or 'Digital Radio Mondiale'. The advantage over analogue SSTV is error correction. That is, with error correction you can get a perfect image of what is sent.

The quality has to be seen to be believed. It is light years ahead of old-style SSTV and the images are top notch.

To receive digital SSTV you will need pretty much the same equipment that you use to receive its analogue equivalent. That is, you need a good, stable HF transceiver (or receiver if you only want to receive), an interface to connect your radio to the computer and some software.

A good program to use is EasyPal (see www.G0HWC.com to download it). G0HWC's web site is a mine of information on SSTV and other interesting ham-related topics.

Once you have download and installed the software you can get going. We suggest that you start with receiving images, to get a feel for how the software works and the protocol for sending and receiving pictures.

If you are itching to start, connect your computer to the audio output of your HF radio and run the EasyPal program. To start, tune to either 7.058MHz LSB or 14.233MHz USB.

Please note that you do need a good signal to decode EasyPal images on 20m, so I suggest starting with 40m (7MHz).

If you are lucky you may hear digital SSTV'ers discussing what they are doing and even getting ready to send an image. If you wait, sooner or later someone will send an image which - while it is being transmitted - sounds like a digital screeching noise.

If you are running EasyPal and it is connected correctly it will automatically start receiving images. Unlike analogue SSTV they won't appear as they are sent, but will display once the whole file has been received. Meanwhile, you can follow the progress of the image file being received in a bar graph across the bottom of the screen. You can also see the signal quality with the 'Sync' lights at the top.

Digital SSTV images are much higher resolution than analogue images.

The EasyPal digital SSTV software in action.

Setting the input sound level is critical and it is worth referring to the EasyPal help files to learn how to do this.

Once the image has been received you may also see some text in the left hand frame, saying who it was from.

To be honest, we have barely scratched the surface of digital SSTV, but you can find out a lot more from the website of VK3EVL.com, which has an extensive help file for EasyPal.

Please don't attempt to transmit any digital SSTV images until you have read all the literature available and you know what you are doing. As a bare minimum you will need to add your callsign to the program and set-up your sound card.

In the meantime, just download a few transmitted images and marvel at the quality.

And yet more digital modes

In this book we have barely scratched the surface of the digital modes available to radio amateurs. There are lots of others, including ROS, which is another week signal mode written by Jose Alberto Ros (EA5HVK); and Olivia, with its multiple musical tones.

There is always something new to play with.

Chapter 9.
A propagation primer

Radio signals travel or propagate from the transmitter to the receiver at the speed of light. Understanding how they propagate at different frequencies will help you make the most of amateur radio.

VHF/UHF Propagation

While HF propagation pundits are concerned with the iono-sphere, VHF/UHF enthusiasts generally have their sights set a little lower – on the troposphere.

Under normal or flat conditions most VHF and UHF communications are generally thought to be line of sight – so the higher your antennas are the better.

Fortunately, reality is actually a little different, thanks to the way VHF and UHF signals can be refracted. This process is the same as that seen with light. Put a pencil in a glass of water and it seems to bend. Look along a hot asphalt road in the middle of summer and it looks like water is in the distance. Both of these phenomena are due to the way that the velocity of light waves change in different media.

Another way of looking at it is that different materials have different refractive indices. The same process applies to radio waves, which are electromagnetic and therefore part of the same 'family' as light waves.

If our radio wave travels from a medium with one refractive index to another, bending or refraction will occur. The amount of bending will depend on the differences in the two refractive indices.

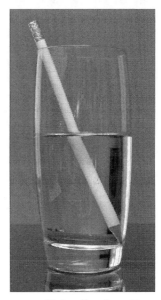

Refraction in action. Radio waves can undergo a similar effect in the troposphere.

Our lower atmosphere isn't a static, single-temperature environment. It is a swirling mass of gases, all at different pressures and different temperatures. There is also varying amounts of water vapour in the atmosphere.

Getting Started in Amateur Radio

As Ian Poole G3YWX points out in the RSGB book *Your Guide To Propagation*, the dielectric constant of air is usually taken to be one, but in reality it varies slightly. The average value is about 1.00030, but it can vary between 1.00027 and 1.00035.

The area of the highest refractive index is usually near the earth. This causes radio waves to bend towards the area of higher refractive index and helps the signal to follow the earth's curvature. The net effect is that VHF and UHF radio signals generally travel around one third further than our strict line of sight calculations suggest they should.

But it gets better!

Tropospheric enhancements

Under certain conditions the refractive index along the path of our signals can increase. If this rate is high enough, signals that would otherwise not follow the curvature of the earth and be lost into space are returned to earth at much greater distances than you would expect.

They can even be trapped in an elevated duct, where they can travel for hundreds of kilometres without being audible on the ground below – a similar effect to having a skip or dead zone on HF.

While these effects are less obvious on the lower bands of the VHF spectrum, they can be very pronounced at 144MHz (2m) and 430MHz (70cm). So how do we predict these and what should we be looking for? As the effects occur in the troposphere it should come as no surprise that it is the weather that affects propagation in this region.

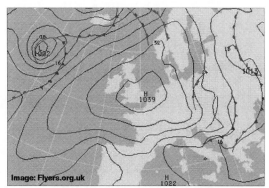

On VHF, look out for high pressure areas, which may bring good conditions.

By studying weather maps and the forecast you should be able to predict when good conditions may occur, although there are always surprises.

One of the main things to look for is a temperature or humidity inversion. Normally the temperature in the troposphere decreases with height, but under certain conditions an inversion can occur with a corresponding sharp change in the refractive index.

Look for a high pressure area over the UK or our near European neighbours. The Met Office has such a useful chart at www.metoffice.gov.uk

Better conditions can occur when a high pressure area is present and particularly in the summer when temperatures are higher and there are higher levels of humidity.

High pressure areas are usually quite stable and good conditions can last for a few days. Oddly, the best conditions can also occur as the pressure starts to fall from a high, so look for high pressure regions in or around Europe and UK, plus a falling barometer.

You can also get a temperature inversion with the approach of a cold front. This occurs as warmer air rises over the colder air beneath it, creating the inversion. This is normally associated with fast-moving fronts, in whch case any lift conditions may be over quickly.

Other inversions in the summer can occur near sunrise, as air at higher altitudes is heated first. Fog and mist in the mornings can also be signs of temperature inversions.

Unfortunately, not all high pressure systems bring good conditions or 'lifts'. It is up to you to monitor other indicators such as beacon and repeater reception.

You can also get enhanced propagation across the sea. Temperature inversions occur frequently along coastal areas bordering large bodies of water. This is the result of the movement of cool, humid air shortly after sunset, when the ground air cools more quickly than the upper air layers. The same action may take place in the morning when the rising sun warms the upper layers. This area can be very close to the water, which means that stations near the water's edge at sea level get good conditions while those on the top of hills don't.

There are other propagation modes available to VHF operators including aurora and meteor scatter. Microwave specialists can also include troposcatter and rain scatter in their armoury.

HF Propagation

When it comes to VHF/UHF we are mostly concerned with the lower portion of the earth's atmosphere – or troposphere. It is the upper portion – or ionosphere – that usually interests us when it comes to HF. And it is the sun that interests HF enthusiasts most of all.

The sun is a massive ball of hydrogen, where protons are forced together at its centre, ultimately fusing into helium and creating vast amounts of energy, just like a hydrogen bomb. The sun drives most of our propagation on HF.

Years ago observers noted that at times there were dark spots on the sun. Although they didn't know it at the time, these sunspots were caused by twisted magnetic fields. They seemed to increase and decrease in a roughly

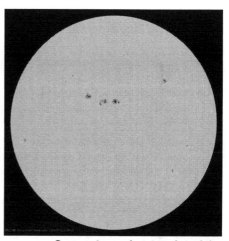

Sunspots are key to a lot of the propagation we get on HF.

eleven-year cycle. These sunspots emit ultra violet and soft X-ray energy that ionises the rarified gases that make up our ionosphere, turning it in a virtual mirror for HF signals. It is these ionospheric layers or regions that allows us to bounce our HF signals around the globe, enabling worldwide communication.

Scientists realised some time ago that during periods of high sunspot activity the ionisation increased. We now have a method of measuring this solar activity. It is called the Solar Flux Index (SFI), which is actually a measure of the intensity of radio waves coming from the sun at a wavelength of 10.7cm. It isn't this radiation that actually causes the ionisation, but there is a strong correlation between the actual UV output and the SFI figure.

As the earth's atmosphere absorbs a lot of the sun's ultra violet light before it ever reaches the earth the SFI is an easier way to measure the sun's relative output at ground level. At the time of writing the SFI was 149. To give you a gauge of how active this is, at sunspot minimum in 2008 the SFI got down to about 65. At the sunspot peak

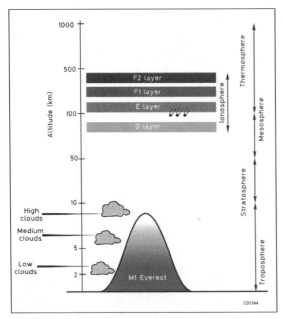

The different layers of the ionosphere play different roles in HF propagation

in January 2014 it reached as high as 237.

A solar flux in excess of 100-120 usually, but not always, brings good conditions on 10m (28 MHz), with inter-continental openings at the right time of year.

The lower HF bands, such as 20m (14MHz), 17m (18MHz) and 15m (21MHz) can usually support long distance communication even with lower SFI figures. Down at 3.5MHz and 7MHz D layer absorption during the day can restrict communications to very short ground-wave distances at times, but both can open-up for long distance communication at night, especially in the winter.

Unfortunately, high sunspot activity can also bring solar flares, which can be devastating for the HF bands, their intense UV/X-ray output causing massive D-layer absorption and therefore poor conditions on HF during the day at times. Being electromagnetic radiation the UV/X-rays hit the ionosphere about eight and half minutes after they leave the sun.

These events are often called Sudden Ionospheric Disturbances (SIDs) and it can be like someone switching off band conditions in an instant, although the ionosphere can recover reasonably quickly.

Solar flares are classed according to their severity, with A, B, C, M or X-class flares according to the peak flux (in watts per square metre, W/m^2) of 1 to 8 ångströms X-rays near Earth.

Each X-ray class category is divided into a logarithmic scale, from 1 to 9. For example: B1 to B9, C1 to C9, M1 to M9. An X2 flare is twice as powerful as an X1 flare, and four times more powerful than an M5 flare. The X-class category is slightly different because it doesn't stop at X9, but continues on. X-class solar flares are the biggest and strongest of them all. Strong radio black-

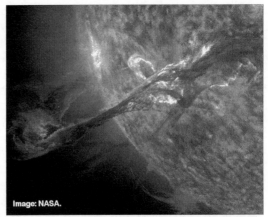

Image: NASA.

A huge Coronal Mass Ejection from the sun.

outs can occur on the daylight side of the Earth during a flare event.

The largest solar flare ever recorded (since satellites started to measure them in 1976) was estimated to be an X28 solar flare, which occurred on 4 November 2003, during solar cycle 23.

Solar flares are often linked to something called a Coronal Mass Ejection (CME), when millions of tonnes of solar matter (or more correctly plasma) is ejected into space at up to 600+ kilometres *per second.* If these CMEs are earth-facing the material released can wreak havoc on our ionosphere.

There are also coronal holes on the sun's surface that can release plasma. The plasma travels much more slowly than the UV and X-ray electromagnetic energy. It can take between 36 and 56 hours to reach the vicinity of Earth – a journey of 93 million miles.

'Slowly' is a relative term, as the solar wind can reach speeds of more than 450km per second, and because these clouds are composed of fast-moving charged particles the plasma carries with it a magnetic field, which interacts with the Earth's magnetic field.

Earth's magnetosphere is a distorted doughnut shaped 'cage', formed by the lines of magnetic force generated in the Earth's core. It protects us from most of what the Sun can throw at us. Without it, the majority of life on Earth could not exist.

If the magnetic field of the plasma is pointing North, the cloud bounces off fairly harmlessly, like similar poles of small bar magnets; but in the opposite direction the field lines of the plasma are said to 'connect' with the geomagnetic field, like the opposite poles of a bar magnet. This situation opens up cracks in Earth's defences and charged particles flood in. The most notable visible effects of this phenomenon are the aurora, seen mainly in high latitudes after a magnetic storm.

The magnetic characteristics of the plasma cloud are referred to as its B field. In particular, we are interested in the field's Z direction, referred to as the 'Bz'. When the Bz is South facing you are more likely to get coupling into the earth's magnetic field, and that is when we can get problems. An event where the fast-moving plasma has a South-facing Bz may cause Earth's magnetic field to vary wildly for a short period, an event that can be observed on magnetometers. It is called a Geomagnetic Storm.

The field strength of the Bz is measured in nanoTeslas, with anything more than about -10 nanoTeslas (the minus sign indicating South) generally causing problems. Incidentally, one nanoTesla is 0.000000001 of a Tesla (the SI unit for magnetic field strength). By comparison, an average MRI machine can develop field strengths of 1.5-3 Tesla.

The majority of the particles are swept past the Earth and are sucked into the long tail of the magnetosphere on the side of Earth opposite to the Sun. The geomagnetic field ultimately draws them back towards the Earth, where they spiral down towards the poles.

This can cause enhanced D layer absorption, especially in the polar regions, making long-range communication difficult on more northerly paths.

A high K index can be a sign that an aurora is in progress.

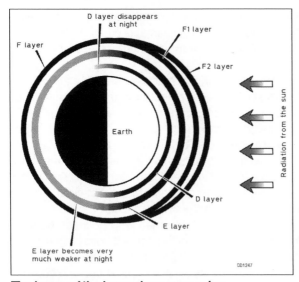

The layers of the ionosphere over a day.

The effect of this incoming material on the Earth's magnetic field is measured by the so-called K Index, which is updated every three hours. The K index is an integer in the range 0-9, with 1 being calm and 5 or more indicating a geomagnetic storm. It is logarithmic, so a change from 1 to 5 is quite extreme.

The A-index provides a daily average level for geomagnetic activity – each three-hourly K index is converted back into a linear scale and averaged. Readings from many magnetometers around the world are aggregated to give planetary A and K index readings, noted by the suffix Ap and Kp. Thus a Kp index of 1 might convert to an Ap index of 4. But a Kp index of 5 might become an Ap index of 48.

So if you want to know what the conditions have been like over the past three hours, look at the Kp index first. The Ap index only gives an indicator for the last 24 hours and may not reflect current conditions very accurately.

Putting this all together, a fast solar wind speed, coupled with a Bz that is pointing South and high particle densities (per cubic centimetre) are generally bad news for HF, but might herald auroral conditions on VHF; whereas a high SFI and a low K index can be good news for HF, especially in the autumn and winter when conditions are generally better than in the summer.

HF propagation is a very technical subject and together with Alan Melia, G3NYK I produced a free e-book about the subject that you can download at http://rsgb.org/main/files/2012/10/Understanding_LF_and_HF_propagation.pdf

Sporadic-E

The period May to mid August is best for Sporadic-E (Es), which can affect signals on all bands from 14-144MHz, although it is most commonly noticed on 28MHz and 50MHz. Sporadic-E openings on 2m are rarer, but they do occur. For example, most summers there are one or two good openings to Spain.

You can listen for these using a portable FM radio. If you are very lucky you may hear foreign language broadcast stations around 100MHz. This is a sign that there could be an opening on 2m as well.

But what is Sporadic-E and how can we predict it?

We know what Sporadic-E is, but its exact causes are still up for debate. It is an unusual form of radio propagation, where signals are refracted or bounced off fast-moving 'clouds' of unusually ionised atmospheric gas in the lower E region (located at altitudes of approximately 90 to 160km).

Short skip Es occurs when patches form in the E-layer of the ionosphere. This layer normally refracts shortwave and medium wave signals, but is transparent to VHF radiation. The ionisation patches drift westwards at speeds of a few hundred km per hour. Es events usually begin mid morning, and there is a peak in the afternoon, with another peak in the evening. Es propagation is usually gone by local midnight.

The cause of Es ionisation is not precisely known. Some people have tried to connect it with thunderstorms, but there are plenty of incidences of Es where no thunderstorms were in the area.

The best theory at the moment is that it is caused by wind shear in the upper atmosphere. You can get very fast-moving winds moving in different directions. Now, inject some ions into these winds and they will be forced up or down as they interact with Earth's magnetic field. You can imagine a situation where some ions are forced upwards and some (in winds moving in the other direction) are forced downwards. The net result is a patch or cloud of ionisation.

These can be relatively long-lived, or come and go quickly. What we do know is that they move quite quickly and the propagation mode is characterised by very strong signals, rapid QSB and signals that appear and disappear from different areas on the ground as the clouds move. The propagation range for single-hop Es is typically 1,000 to 2,000km, but the distances can be increased with multi-hop Es.

Now you are probably wondering where these ions come from in the first place. One theory is that they are heavy metallic ions from meteor debris. Jim Bacon, G3YLA, who is a professional meteorologist, has looked very closely at Sporadic-E and has also managed to link it with weather patterns and high-level winds moving across the mountainous areas of Europe, including the Alps, the Harz mountains and the Pyrenees. He thinks that these winds over the mountains create gravity waves that move upwards, helping to compress the ionisation.

There is still room for research on Es, but for the new radio ham how do you make the most of Sporadic E?

Firstly, keep an eye on 28MHz and 50MHz from May to late August. These will be the first bands to show the effects of Es. If you are away from the radio, also check out www.dxmaps.com which has real-time maps of Es and other activity.

As I said, there are occasionally Es openings on 2m in the summer, but they are quite rare. You can also look out for VHF Es openings by using a simple FM broadcast radio. A few days each summer you can get a situation where Spanish broadcast stations sud-

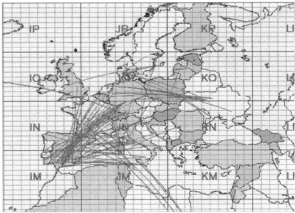

DXMaps.com is an excellent resource for keeping an eye on Sporadic-E (Es) openings.

denly appear out of nowhere on the FM band between 88-108MHz.

These openings can be fleeting, but when they do occur the stations are very strong and can even override more local FM stations.

Using HF beacons to gauge propagation conditions

So how can you work out what parts of the world an HF band is open to in only three minutes? The answer is to listen to the International Beacon Project, run by the Northern California DX Foundation (NCDXF).

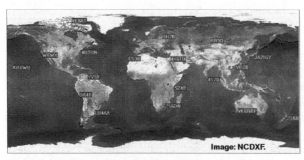

Image: NCDXF.

The International Beacon Project lets you check propagation conditions worldwide in minutes.

The NCDXF, in cooperation with the International Amateur Radio Union (IARU), constructed and operates a worldwide network of high-frequency radio beacons on 14.100, 18.110, 21.150, 24.930, and 28.200MHz.

The beacons are in USA (New York, California and Hawaii), Canada, New Zealand, Australia, Japan, Russia, Hong Kong, Sri Lanka, South Africa, Kenya, Israel, Finland, Madeira, Argentina, Peru and Venezuela, although some may be off the air at times due to maintenance/failure. You can find out the current state of all the beacons at any time by going to www.ncdxf.org

Each beacon transmits in turn – a 10-second sequence every three minutes. Once they have sent their sequence on, say, 14MHz, the beacon moves up to 18MHz and repeats it and another beacon takes up their slot on 14MHz.

These beacons help you assess the current condition of the ionosphere. All you have to do is listen on the beacon frequencies and copy the CW callsigns of the various beacons to figure out where that band is open to. Because the beacons transmit at known times it is easy to work out which beacon is transmitting without actually knowing Morse code. To discover which beacon is transmitting, see the schedule or use a computer program like 'BeSpeak' by G0TLK. Just Google it.

The beacons starts to transmit at 100W, before stepping down to 10W, 1W and 100mW in one-second steps. You may be surprised, but it is really easy to hear some of the beacons transmitting at 100mW – which is 1,000th the full power of 100 Watts!

So how can you help the beacon project? Just make sure you don't transmit on or near any of the beacon frequencies listed. Please check the bandplan at rsgb.org

You can find out more about the beacons, including how to conduct unattended propagation research using a program called Faros, at www.ncdxf.org

Once you step away from the NCDXF beacon chain, coverage can be a little more patchy. Take a look at

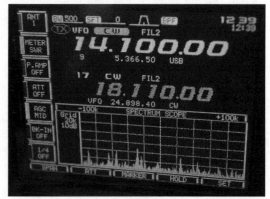

Make sure you keep away from transmitting on the International Beacon Project frequencies.

G3USF's Worldwide List of HF Beacons at www.keele.ac.uk/depts/por/28.htm and you'll see what I mean.

IARU Region 1 discourages beacon operation from 1.8 to 10MHz, but even so there are quite a few on these bands that are active. These can be quite interesting to track down, as their power output ranges from 0.1 to 100 watts. For example, SK6RUD on 10.133MHz in Oxaback, southern Sweden, is regularly heard, even though it only runs 0.5W to a quarter wave vertical antenna. SK6RUD has 500kHz and 3.5424MHz beacons too, but it is the 30m one that you most likely to hear during the day from the UK. It sometimes has its 24.912MHz beacon running too.

Step up to 28MHz though and the world is your oyster. There are literally hundreds of 10m beacons between 28.110 and 28.322MHz and tracking them all can become a full-time hobby. Again, many of them are very low powered, typically between 5 and 10 watts. If the solar flux index (SFI) is above 100-120 and it is autumn/winter it is relatively easy to hear some of the US beacons - mainly during the afternoons.

In the summer, Sporadic-E brings in lots of beacons from all over Europe.

Much of what I have said applies equally to 50MHz (6m), where there are beacons all around the world. See www.keele.ac.uk/depts/por/50.htm for details.

Beacon hunting can become addictive, but don't forget to call CQ as well. The beacons tell you that there is propagation to a particular part of the world, but it is up to you to make the band active.

Using HF propagation prediction software

HF propagation prediction software can help you plan your radio operations. That is, if you are trying to contact the east coast of the USA on, say, 14MHz in October, a quick look at some software will quickly show you that the afternoon or early evening are the best times. If you didn't know that you could end up calling CQ for hours and get nowhere!

There are a number of ways of finding out what band is open to where and when. The

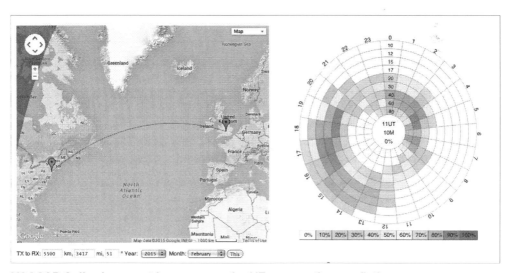

VOACAP Online is a great free resource for HF propagation predictions.

first is to use the excellent VOACAP Online site at www.voacap.com, which will quickly show you the best band to use for any time of day. VOACAP Online uses the VOACAP software as its back end, but I can't recommend that you use it on your own computer as it is very complex.

However, other people have written software that uses the same VOACAP 'engine', so if you do want to have your own PC-based prediction software there is plenty to choose from.

Here are some options:

VOAProp by G4ILO

VOAProp, written by Julian Moss, G4ILO (now sadly a silent key) is free and works with VOACAP to give a visual display on your PC of HF paths. It is very easy to use and can be configured to either see what parts of the world your signals are likely to reach or to work out the best time for a specific path.

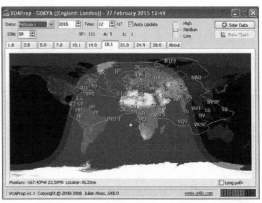

It has a very neat graphical inter-face and can also be configured to show you in real time which IBP beacon is op-erating. It will also show you the sunset/ sunrise terminator on the globe.

See www.g4ilo.com/voaprop.html

VOAProp is an excellent free PC program for predictions.

HamCap

This is also free and works together with VOACAP to give visual propagation predictions. It can also be used with DX Atlas (not free). It has a small unobtrusive window and can be adapted to suit any hams, from someone with a dipole and 10W to an amateur with a three-element Yagi and 400W.

I use this to produce my monthly HF propagation forecasts at g0kya.blogspot.com
See www.dxatlas.com/hamcap/

W6ELProp

Another free PC program. This is getting a little old now, but it is very good and can be much better at predicting 80m propagation openings than VOACAP, which was never designed to work at frequencies as low as 3.5MHz.

See www.qsl.net/w6elprop/

ACE-HF Pro

This package costs $199, but is one of the best prediction programs around. It has lots of features and is excellent at working out the best time to make a contact on any given path. It might not be suitable for beginners, but it can be very useful for more experienced amateurs.

See www.longwaveinc.com/ace/ace-hf-pro/

ASAPS v6

The full version of ASAPS costs AUD385 (around £221). There is also a Lite version for AUD95 (about £55). ASAPS uses a statistical analysis of ionosonde readings. ASAPS Lite enables you to quickly generate daily frequency plans and area prediction results in graphical form. There is also a free demo version.

See www.ips.gov.au

There are lots of other HF prediction software packages around, but the ones listed here are the most commonly used. We suggest you start with one of the free ones, perhaps VOAProp, and see how you get on.

You can also use the monthly HF predictions charts in *RadCom*, which are also available online at http://rsgb.org/main/operating/propagation-predictions/

Chapter 10.
DXing, Contesting, QSLing and Awards

Introduction to HF and VHF DXing

Amateur radio operations can fall into a number of camps. One is talking to local stations, while another is talking to amateurs in other countries. For many the ultimate is chasing DX, but what exactly is DX?

Ask different people and you will probably get different answers. To most amateurs it means a contact that is either rare or a long way away. For example, if you use 2m (145MHz) you can probably talk to people within about a 25-50 mile radius, but if the right tropospheric conditions exist you might be able to talk to the Netherlands, Germany or Norway. That would be probably be classed as DX on 2m or the higher UHF and microwave bands, but if you were on 40m (7MHz), being able to work stations

What is DX? This operation on Desecheo Island definitely counts.

in Europe could be a daily occurrence and wouldn't count as DX. But what if you could work New Zealand (ZL) on 40m? Now, that is far less likely and could definitely be classed as DX. You would probably be very pleased to work ZL on 40m.

Many radio amateurs try to work as many countries or 'entities' as they can. There are even awards available for doing just that, such as the ARRL's DXCC (DX Century Club) award for working 100 different entities.

But what exactly is an entity? Generally, radio hams talk about working people in other countries, but we use the word 'entity' rather then country as some are not really countries in their own right.

Take Market Reef (callsign prefix OJ) for example. It is a tiny island situated midway between Sweden and Finland. In fact the island is split in two, with both countries owning roughly half. By having its own callsign prefix this makes it very valuable to hams who want to work as many entities as possible. Market Reef is therefore an entity – separate from Sweden and Finland – and is often visited by radio amateurs on so-called DXpeditions. A DXpedition is where one or more hams get together specifically to travel to a rare entity to activate it on the amateur bands.

Some countries can consist of many DXCC entities, depending on their geographical make-up. Other entities are classed as rare DX, even if they aren't that far away. The Sovereign Military Order of Malta (which is actually in Rome) could be classed as DX, as there are generally few operations from there. Allocated the callsign prefix 1A, there is usually a big 'pile-up' or scrum to make contact, whenever anyone operates from 1A.

The recent DXpediton to Navassa Island in the Caribbean was a perfect example of everyone wanting to work a rare DX entity. Navassa is a United States island, just west of Haiti. It is rare because there hadn't been a DXpedition to Navassa in 22 years, and there is unlikely to be another for another ten, so everyone wanted to work its callsign K1N on *all* the HF bands, as they would otherwise have little or no chance to work it again for some time.

This QSL card from T32C on Kiritimati confirms a DX contact.

There are currently 340 DXCC entities on the ARRL DXCC entities list, although not all of them are active at the same time. Some of the more exotic Pacific Islands, or even parts of the Antarctic, may only be activated once very 10-20 years.

That's what makes amateur radio so interesting. You can try to work as many entities as possible on all the bands, or see how many you can work on just one band. The ultimate is to try and work 100 or more entities on *each* of the five main HF bands – a so called 5-band DXCC.

You can set your own goals or have a competition with friends or fellow members of your local radio club.

Understanding squares, locators and zones

When you first get on the air it can be very confusing. Sooner or later someone is going to ask you what your WAB square is, or your Locator, or in a contest, what Zone you are in. These are all methods of letting the other person know where you are located, but what do they all mean and why do you need to know?

Location information is used a lot in amateur radio. It can be used to work out the distance between two stations, or it can be used to collect awards. In some contests you get extra points for working specific Zones, so it pays to know where you are!

Let's take a look at what they all mean.

Maidenhead or QTH Locator squares

Maidenhead or QTH Locator squares are mainly used on VHF, UHF and micro-waves to plot where stations are. For example, the field IO (Italy Oscar) covers the Western part of the UK, Scotland and Ireland.

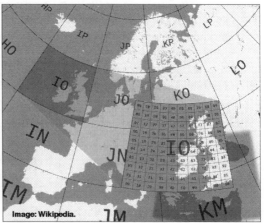

Image: Wikipedia.

If you operate on VHF you'll need to know your Maidenhead Locator.

The field is then broken down into numbered squares that give more information as to your whereabouts – each of these squares represents 1° of latitude by 2° of longitude. Finally, two further letters define it even more.

For example, my locator is JO02NN.

If you want to calculate what square you are, in the easiest way is to go to http://f6fvy.free.fr/qthLocator/, zoom in on the map and click where you live.

If you chase DX on 6m, 2m, 70cms or higher, the chances are people will want to know your Locator.

Worked All Britain square

The Worked All Britain Awards Group (WAB) was devised by the late John Morris, G3ABG in 1969. The aim was to promote an interest in amateur radio in Britain and sponsor a series of awards based on the geography of Great Britain and Northern Ireland. You can find out more at www.worked-all-britain.co.uk

In the meantime you might want to work out what WAB square you live in. These are based on the Ordnance Survey maps of the UK and I've found that the easiest way is to go to www.streetmap.co.uk and enter your postcode.

Once you have done this you'll see a line at the bottom of the screen that says 'Click here to convert coordinates'. If you do you will see that the sixth line down is headed 'LR', standing for Land Ranger. Now just take the two letters, plus the first and fourth number (out of the six digits). This is your WAB square. As a test, enter my postcode – NR18 0XJ – and you will see that the WAB square comes out as TG10. Now input your postcode and see what your WAB square is.

ITU Zones and CQ Zones

If you enter HF contests you may hear people exchanging Zone numbers. This can be very confusing, as it depends what contest you are in as to what your Zone is.

For example, the ITU (International Telecommunication Union) has the UK in ITU region 27.

However, *CQ* magazine has its own zones, which are used in its contests such as

CQ Worldwide. The CQ zone for Western Europe is 14.

Just to confuse you even more, we live in IARU (International Amateur Radio Union) Region 1!

Your best bet is make a note of all of your location information, so that you can refer to it when operating. If using 6m, 2m or higher you will likely be asked for your Maidenhead or QTH Locator. If anyone asks for your WAB square you will also have it to hand. You will probably only need your Zone information if operating in a contest.

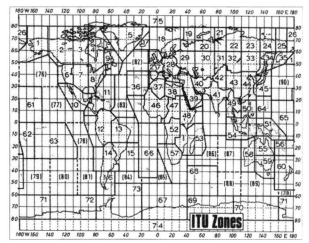

Confusingly, the UK is in ITU Zone 27 and CQ Zone 14.

Working a DXpedition

As we've said, a DXpedition is an organised trip to a far-flung part of the world that is often very rare to hear, from an amateur radio point of view. NG3K in the US maintains a list of upcoming DXpeditions – see www.ng3k.com.

If you want to work a DXpedition the first thing to do is plan, plan and plan again. Find out when they will be active, on what bands and what modes. Then use a propagation prediction program (see the Propagation chapter) or ClubLog (www.clublog.org) to work out the best times to try for them on each band, and make sure you have a suitable antenna.

Once the DXpedition is under way the DX Cluster, such as www.dxsummit.fi, will show if they active, so listen on the bands to see if you can hear them.

RSGB has a guide to working DX on its web site in the 'Getting started' section. It is worth reading carefully as there are some subtle differences when working a DXpedition than when you are just chatting on the bands.

Firstly, they are likely to be working split frequency. That is, they will be transmitting on one frequency and lis-

Keep an eye on the DX Cluster to see what bands a DXpedition is on.

tening on another. Often the DX station will say something like 'listening up' or 'listening up five', This means, for example, that they are transmitting on 14.210MHz and listening on 14.215MHz. This in turn means you need to find out how to work split with your transceiver.

Getting Started in Amateur Radio

Some of the bigger DXpeditions will say 'listening up', but won't say where. The trick then is to try and find where they are listening, by finding the other station sending its report. This might be two or three kHz away, but it could be up to 50kHz away (as was the case for the K1N DXpedition to Navassa Island).

To make life even more difficult, sometimes the DXpedition will work a station and then move up or down the band to the next one. The real challenge then is to work out which way they are moving and anticipate where they might be listening next. Working a DXpedition can turn into a complex chase!

A DXpedition may want to work specific regions only, such as North America. If so they will announce this by saying something like 'CQ CQ CQ VK9DLX North America only'. If they are asking for Japanese stations only and you call from the UK you won't be very popular - and they probably won't work you either - so make sure you plan your activity to optimise your chances of contacting your target DXpedition. It is never going to be easy, but that's what makes the hobby so challenging and interesting.

How computer logging can help you

When you first get your licence you may not bother to keep a log of your contacts. After all, Ofcom removed the need for UK radio amateurs to keep a log some time ago.

However, most amateurs find a log book very useful. Not only can you keep note of your contacts and the countries you have worked, but it can come in handy if there are any complaints about interference. Your log will tell you and Ofcom what band you were on, or even if you were transmitting at all.

A paper log is both inexpensive and easy to keep, but ultimately you might want to consider a computer log. Software is available for PCs, Macs, iPads, Android and Linux,

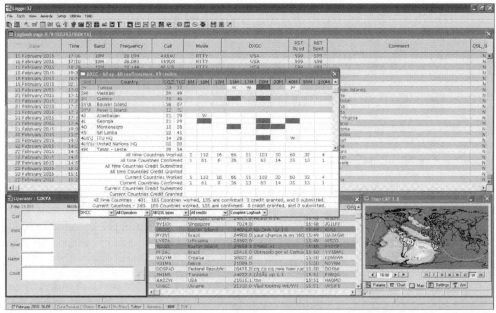

A program like Logger32 can also keep track of any award you are chasing, such as DXCC.

and packages vary from free to paid for.

For Windows users, popular choices are Logger 32, Log4OM and XMLog. On the Mac there are fewer choices, but look at MacLoggerDX, Aether and SkookumLogger (which is really designed for contests).

But which one should you plump for? The best thing is to ask your fellow hams what they use. They will know the foibles of their particular software and might even be able to help you set it up. If you don't know any other hams there is a good range of log reviews at www.eham.net.

One advantage of an electronic log is that it can automatically keep tabs on the stations you have worked and on what bands. It can also tell you if you have worked someone before. Just putting their callsign in is usually enough for the log to instantly show any previous QSOs you may have had.

Most electronic logging software packages will also print labels for your QSL cards, keep track of your progress on any awards you are chasing, upload information to the ARRL's Logbook of the World system and much more.

If you are chasing awards a computer log will tell you instantly how many countries or entities you have worked and on what bands. It then becomes easier to see what else you need to work and where.

Computer logging also makes it easier to use electronic QSL services, such as eQSL.net. All you have to do is create an ADIF file from your log and upload it to the service.

ADIF stands for Amateur Data Interchange Format and is an open standard for the exchange of data between ham radio software. The other great thing about ADIF files is that if you decide you want to try another logging package it is really easy to import your complete log into the new software.

A smart move is to make a back up of your log in ADIF format on a regular basis and keep a copy on a back-up disk or with an online service like Dropbox. That way you will never lose it.

Although setting up a computer log may seem daunting at first you will soon realise that it is a major boon, indeed you'll wonder how you ever managed without one.

How to send and receive QSL cards

If you are start chasing DX you are going to want to collect QSL cards too. Sending and receiving QSL cards is a traditional part of the amateur radio hobby. Even in these days of the Internet and e-mail, many hams enjoy collecting QSLs. They confirm that a contact was made (which can be essential for some awards) and the cards can be very attractive in their own right.

The term QSL comes from the international Q code and means "'I confirm receipt of your transmission'. A QSL card is therefore a written confirmation.

The sending of QSL cards dates back to the 1920s, when AM radio broadcasts were still a novelty and stations wanted to know how far away they were being received. Radio amateurs were quick to adopt the exchange of QSL cards and many of the older cards are now highly sought after.

Each card contains details about one or more contacts, the station and its operator. This usually includes the call sign of both stations participating in the contact, the time and date when it occurred (usually specified in UTC), the radio frequency or band used, the mode of transmission, and a signal report.

The International Amateur Radio Union and its member societies recommend a maximum size of 3½ by 5½ inches (140 mm by 90 mm) for the card, although some cards (especially from rare DXpeditions) can be a gate-fold design with multiple pages.

Cards do not have to be pictorial – some are just plain text. Others have a photograph of the operator, or his local- ity or interests.

There are many specialist QSL printers around, or you can create and print your own if you don't think you will be sending many.

There are two ways of sending and receiving physical QSL cards – via a bureau or direct.

The author's own QSL card.

QSLing via the Bureau

The Bureau is the easiest and cheapest way to send and receive cards. RSGB members send their cards to the central Bureau, where they are then sorted and despatched around the world. To receive cards RSGB members can lodge self addressed, stamped enve- lopes with a sub-manager who looks after their callsign series. The sub manager will collect together cards that are sent in via the Bureau and send them to the member on a regular basis. Note the address to which you send your envelopes to receive cards will not be the same as the address you use when sending cards!

When sending cards, each batch should contain proof of RSGB membership that is no more than three months old. This is usually the address label and identification num- bers cut from the bag used to post *RadCom*. When sending cards you should sort them in a specific way – see the QSL section of www.rsgb.org for more details.

When receiving cards the bureau operates on a quarterly system of operation, so if you have received any cards in a given three month period your sub-manager will send them to you. If you receive lots of cards you may receive your envelopes more regularly and of course if there are no cards nothing will be sent. It is usual to lodge a number of stamped, C5 self-addressed envelopes with your sub-manager, with '1 of 5', '2 of 5' etc marked on them so that you'll know when you need to send new ones. Standard enve- lopes sent through the Royal Mail can usually accommodate 5mm or 5-10 QSL cards. If you receive more cards than this it is best to add a large letter stamp which allows up to thickness of 25mm of cards to be posted. Stamps should be marked either 1st or 2nd class, not specific postage amounts.

There are various QSL sub-managers who look after specific callsign ranges – you will need to check to see who looks after you.

If you operate more than one callsign or have moved on from a callsign and still want to receive cards you must ensure the RSGB knows what these additional callsigns are. You will also need to supply envelopes for all the callsigns you want to receive cards for. To advise the RSGB of changes to your callsign this can be done easily by visiting www.rsgb.org/amend.

Non members of the RSGB can receive QSLs via the RSGB Bureau, but there is a charge for doing so. Non members cannot send cards through the Bureau. Both services are free of charge to RSGB members, as part of the membership benefits they receive.

You can find out more about QSLing on the special QSL services page on the RSGB web site (www.rsgb.org).

QSLing Direct

Some people prefer to get their QSL cards direct from the station they worked. This may be because it is a rare country and they want to make sure they get the card or because they are chasing an award and need the card as soon as possible.

In either case you can send your card, along with a self-addressed envelope direct to the station or their QSL manager (some stations have someone else handle their cards for them).

If QSLing direct, enclose a self-addressed envelope with your address in full, including your country. Enclose International Reply Coupons (IRCs), Dollars (at least two), or a stamped self-addressed envelope SSAE (if UK cards) to cover return postage costs.

To a large extent, US Dollars are a universally-accepted method of payment for QSL cards, but they are prone to being stolen when sent

Some DXpeditions allow you to order your QSL cards online via OQRS. You need to work them first though!

to some countries. IRCs are popular but are no longer available from UK post offices – don't get caught out buying secondhand IRCs that may not work.

Some DXpeditions now offer a facility where you can pay for your QSL card online and have it delivered directly. This Online QSL service or OQRS is relatively new, but as long as you are in their log it is a quick way of getting a card sent to you – albeit a potentially expensive one.

You can also request a card via OQRS to be sent via the bureau, which may be free or you could be asked for a donation to offset the cost of the DXpedition.

QSL hints and tips
- Check the time in UTC/date/call on your cards are correct.
- Use the route given by the operator or listed on QRZ.com. The operator may tell you to QSL direct only or via his manager.
- Use dark envelopes for your outgoing and return envelopes if QSLing direct. That is, envelopes that are not see through. Money has been known to go missing!
- Ensure that your return envelope is big enough. Miniature envelopes are too small.
- Write the date out in full – eg 12th October 2012. Shortened date formats can be misunderstood. That is, 12-10-12 means 12th October to UK amateurs, but 10th

December to Americans. You could have your card returned with 'NIL' written on it – 'Not in Log'.

- If your QSL is double sided, is your call printed on both sides? If the call is on one side and the information is on the other, it can slow down processing at the Bureau.
- Is your address clear on your card/envelope? If it can't be read it might not come back.
- Is your county/Locator/WAB square/IOTA number on your card? Many recipients of your card may want them for awards.
- Don't send foreign stamps – they could be out of date. IRCs or US Dollars are better currency.

Electronic QSL cards

Because of the cost of sending and receiving QSL cards via the mail there has been a rise in interest in so-called electronic QSLing. With these systems you can design a 'card' online and then upload your electronic logbook in ADIF format. You then receive 'cards' from your contacts who have done the same – but only if the contacts match; that is the date, time, band and mode you claim you made the contact on are the same as the other station's.

EQSL is another way to receive cards, but this time they arrive electronically.

Note that this form of QSL is often not accepted for some awards- eg ARRL's DXCC (DX Century Club) and RSGB's awards. But some, like the EQSL system (www.eqsl.cc), have their own award systems that are very popular.

The ARRL has its own electronic QSL system called Logbook of the World. With this you don't get a physical or even an electronic card, but if your uploaded details match those of the station you claim to have worked you get a 'credit' that can be used for ARRL awards. Logbook of the World is quite complex and the best thing to do is read all about it on the ARRL website (www.arrl.org).

Contesting or Radio Sport

Contesting or Radio Sport enjoys a large and loyal following with radio amateurs. Radio Sport usually involves a competition to see who can contact the most stations in a set period of time on certain band(s) and within specific rules.

Love it or loathe it, contesting gives you the opportunity to hone your operating skills and tweak your equipment to get the best results. If you have never taken part in a contest before then there is one way that you can dip your toe in the water – and perhaps help out your local club at the same time.

Contests all have one thing in common – on MF/HF they only take part on the 160m (1.8MHz), 80m (3.5MHz), 40m (7MHz), 20m (14MHz), 15m (21MHz) and 10m (28MHz) bands. There are no contests on the so-called WARC bands of 30m (10MHz), 17m (18MHz) and 12m (12MHz), which were allocated to radio amateurs at the 1979 World Administrative Radio Conference (hence the term WARC). This means that if you don't want to take part in a contest, perhaps on a weekend which is when most contests take place, you might like to head to one of the WARC bands. You'll find a comprehensive list of contests due to take place at www.sk3bg.se/contest/

Contesting, or Radio Sport, has grown in popularity over the years.

Contests can be cut and thrust events, and it is best to cut your teeth on an easy one first, Luckily there is one in the UK that fits the bill nicely. Each year the 80m Club Championship (80m CC) runs from February to July. The event is a series of short weekday evening contests on 80m that aim to promote competition between RSGB affiliated societies and clubs. Individual scores in every event count towards your club or society's overall score, so the more members that take part the better the club does.

But what does contesting entail? Firstly, the 80m CC events all take place on 80m (3.5MHz), so you will need a transceiver that operates on that band. You will also need an antenna. Don't worry if you can't get a full-size dipole up at 100ft, because a lot of entrants use shorter antennas like G5RVs, W5GI Mystery Antennas (see the antenna chapter) and Inverted Ls, some of them in less than ideal locations.

The important thing is to try and use a horizontally-polarised antenna, if possible. This is because you will be trying to work around the UK and a vertical antenna won't really give you the best radiation pattern. Although the event is aimed at UK operators you often get stations from the Netherlands, Germany, Sweden and even Lithuania joining in for fun.

The 80m Club Championship uses SSB, data modes and CW, so there is something for everyone. There are two classes of power output – up to 100 watts (Low) and up to 10 watts (QRP), so Foundation licensees can take part. The events take place between 8pm and 9.30pm local time on Monday, Wednesday and Thursday evenings. You can find a calendar of the events at www.rsgbcc.org/hf/ One week it might be SSB, the next week data and the following CW etc. On the data evenings there is usually a mixture of RTTY, PSK 31 and PSK63 being used.

So what do you do? If you are new to contesting the best thing to do is listen. You will see that contestants pass a signal report and a serial number, starting from 001 and incrementing upwards.

A typical SSB exchange might go like this:

(Them)	CQ contest, CQ contest, this is G4ABC.
(You)	M6ABC
(Them)	M6ABC – thanks, you are 599 005
(You)	Thanks – you are 599 001
(Them)	Many thanks – CQ contest (etc)

Getting Started in Amateur Radio

And that's it. No name, location or other niceties, just a report and serial number. On data and CW the reports are even shorter, as you will see if you tune into some of the signals during the next contest.

You can keep a paper log, which records the call details and serial number you handed out and received, or you can use a computer logging program like N1MM, or EI5DI's SD Log, both of which are free. This a better way to do it, as you can then output a 'Cabrillo' file and upload it to the RSGB website. Cabrillo is a specific file format that your electronic contest logging software is able to generate.

If you are just dipping your toe in the water with the 80m CC, it is a good idea to (a) read the rules on the RSGB web site (www.rsgb.org) and (b) if possible, get some help from someone at your local club. The most important thing to do is listen and learn before jumping in.

The 80m Club Championships are great fun and a good grounding for the myriad of other contests that take place each week.

How to get a DXCC award

If you are a relative newcomer to amateur radio you may not have heard of the DXCC Award programme. The DX Century Club Award, to give it its full name, is run by the Amateur Radio Relay League (ARRL) in the USA and is generally considered to be *the* award for amateurs to aim for.

The scheme has been running since the 1930s and has been refined over 70 years or so. At the base level, the DXCC is awarded to any radio amateur who has worked and confirmed contact with 100 or more 'entities'.

Now you might think it would be quite easy to work 100 entities out of a list of 340, but that isn't the case. In any one year there may be only around 290 activated in total, and at any one time far fewer than that.

Nevertheless, working 100 entities can be done relatively easily, depending upon how much effort you are prepared to put in, although getting the contacts confirmed may be harder.

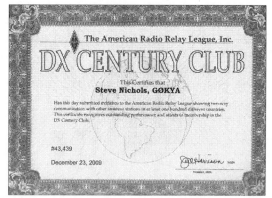

For many hams, DXCC is the ultimate goal. Five-band DXCC takes a lot of effort and time.

Traditionally, DXCC applications were made using QSL cards to confirm the contacts. You received your QSLs either via the bureau or direct, by sending an envelope, International Reply Coupons or Dollar bills to the DX station. While this is still the case with many contacts (and very frustrating it can be when you get no reply!) the ARRL's Logbook of the World (LoTW) is making life easier.

With LoTW you upload your logs via the Internet to the ARRL, as does the DX station. If there is a match with the QSO you get credited with that contact and therefore the entity. This makes life a lot easier and as LoTW has gained in popularity, with more amateurs using it, it is fast becoming the best way to aim for a DXCC award. There isn't enough space here to describe all the intricacies of LoTW, but you can find out more at www.arrl.org/logbook-of-the-world.

Once you have worked and confirmed more than 100 entities on the HF bands you can apply for and claim the basic DXCC award. This can be via submitted QSL cards (which have to be physically checked) or via an LoTW submission. There is a fee for a DXCC submission and the amount varies depending upon how you apply, but it could be as little as $12 if you use LoTW (and are an ARRL member).

The basic DXCC award can be gained using any of the main HF bands with any mode – this gets you the 'mixed' award. You can also apply for a whole host of awards that use a single mode, eg SSB or CW, or where you have worked 100 entities on just one band. There are also endorsements if you work more entities, in blocks of 50.

The pinnacle is the so-called five-band DXCC, where you have worked at least 100 entities on each of the five HF bands of 80, 40, 20, 15 and 10m. And if you can work and confirm at least 331 entities you can get on the ARRL Honor Roll, which is an indication that you really have made it to the top!

A quick tip – if you are serious about getting DXCC the easiest way to do it is to take part in contests like CQ Worldwide (CQWW) in the autumn. There will be hundreds of stations on all over the world, all eager to make contact with you.

DXCC is a complex award programme and we have only just scratched the surface here. To find out more go to www.arrl.org/dxcc-award-information.

A propagation primer

Chapter 11.
What else is there?

Amateur radio is a 'broad church' as they say, with more than enough interesting niches to keep everyone happy. In fact there are so many interesting facets to the hobby that it is impossible to cover them all in this book. For example, you could get into satellite communications – using low-earth orbiting satellites to contact other radio amateurs on VHF, UHF or microwave. At the time of writing there were even plans for an amateur radio transponder to be carried aboard the future Es'hailsat-2 geostationary satellite.

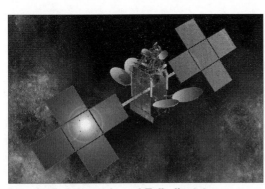

An artist's impression of Es'hailsat-2.

When launched it will have transponders with a 2400MHz uplink and 10GHz downlink, promising to be able to link Brazil with India and all countries in between.

The Qatari-owned Es'hailsat-2 is expected to launch at the end of 2016.

Radio amateurs interested in satellite operation are encouraged to join AMSAT-UK – see amsat-uk.org

Or what about the Vintage and Military Amateur Radio Society (VMARS)? If you are interested in the conservation, restoration and use of classic electronic equipment you would be in good company if you joined VMARS.

VMARS has an ever growing archive of manuals, circuit diagrams, magazines and other historic literature. Currently around 10,000 items are physically stored in its archive, held at the Thorpe Camp Museum in Lincolnshire, once home to the legendary 617 squadron Dam Busters at RAF Woodhall Spa.

To find out more visit www.vmars.org.uk

Or what if you like mountain climbing and hill walking? Summits on the Air (SOTA) is an award scheme for radio amateurs and shortwave listeners that encourages portable operation in mountainous areas. Each week hardy radio amateurs venture up hills around the UK and further afield, and endeavour to make contacts from summits. But you don't need to be a keen fitness fanatic to take part – the scheme even has a category for SOTA chasers, who prefer to stay in their warm shacks! See www.sota.org.uk for more details.

As you can see there really is something for everyone. Now let's take a closer look at just four other interesting elements of the hobby.

Summits on the Air combines amateur radio with healthy outdoor pursuits.

Microwaves

When they are first licensed most radio amateurs tend to concentrate on 2m (144MHz), 70cm (430MHz) and MF/HF (1.8-30MHz). You may think that the higher microwave bands are only for short range, line of sight contacts, but you'd be wrong.

Typical ranges for the most common propagation modes on microwave can cover much of Europe from the UK, and using more advanced modes like moonbounce, half the world can be worked with far more reliability than HF. That's not to say that advanced microwave operation is easy - you have to learn to walk before you can run!

Microwave operation is a facet of the hobby that encourages home construction and experimentation. A lot of the equipment cannot be bought off the shelf, so it appeals to people who like building things.

John, G4BAO and Sam, G4DDK wrote a feature for *RadCom*, the RSGB's monthly magazine, where they concentrated on two of most popular microwave bands – 1.2GHz and 10GHz. This is a summary of what they wrote:

"The UK 1.2GHz (23cm) band covers from 1240MHz to 1325MHz, with 1296MHz to 1298MHz allocated to weak signal DX modes; 1260MHz to 1270MHz is allocated to the amateur satellite service (earth to space direction) and other parts of the band have been allocated, variously, to data links, amateur TV and repeaters.

"Very few 23cm band amateur radio transceivers have been made available and most of those have usually included 23cm band as an option. There are a few dedicated 23cm band transceivers, including the Icom IC-1271 and IC-1275. VHF/UHF multi-band rigs with 23cm include the Icom IC-910X, IC-9100X, Kenwood TS-2000X and the Yaesu FT-736. Of these only the Icom IC-9100X and Kenwood TS-2000X were still in production as this book was written. All of these radios are multimode and include SSB, FM and CW modulation modes.

"A number of FM-only 23cm

John G4BAO operating 10GHz while portable.

John G4BAO - 10GHz microwave

band transceivers have also appeared, including the Yaesu FT-912R, FT-2311, FT-2312, Icom IC-1200, IC-2500 and IC-3700. Kenwood produced the TM-521, TS-531 and TM-541, while Alinco have also produced a 23cm band FM handheld. More recently Icom have introduced a range of D-STAR transceivers with 23cm band capability.

"Outside of these radios a transverter is a good option. A transverter is a combined transmit frequency up-converter and receive frequency down-converter. A lower frequency transceiver is then used as an intermediate frequency (IF) radio, such as 2m (144MHz). Ready-built transverters are available, but many people also build their own. In almost all cases an external power amplifier is required in order to produce output powers in excess of 25W.

"The 23cm band is one where a bit more power can help enormously in making longer distance contacts.

"Antennas for 1.2GHz tend to be Yagis, although dishes, corner reflectors and flat plate designs are also used. Most activity on this band uses horizontal polarisation, rather than vertical polarisation. This is largely historic and resulted from extensive testing that showed horizontal polarisation achieved lower loss over hills and other obstructions as well as better penetration of valleys and other difficult locations.

"The other main microwave band of interest is 10GHz. Here you will definitely not find a transceiver built by the larger radio manufacturers.

"In the UK the 10GHz (3cm) band consists of three sub-bands, from 10000 to 10125MHz, 10225 to 10450 and 10450 to 10500MHz. 10368 to 10370 is allocated to weak signal DX modes, 10450MHz to 10500MHz is allocated to the amateur satellite service (earth to space direction), with the top 25MHz of this sub-band allocated to satellites only. Other parts of the band are allocated, variously, to data links and repeaters.

"10GHz operation may be a challenge for the microwave newcomer, but don't be put off by this. It would be sensible to gain some experience on 144 or 432MHz first, before venturing higher. You can then seek out active microwavers, by joining a group such as the UK Microwave Group (www.microwavers.org) and learn from them.

"By far the best, easiest and cheapest way to get a feel for 10GHz is with a receive-only system consisting of a frequency down-converter using a surplus satellite LNB with a cheap USB dongle designed for TV reception, and a software defined radio (SDR) program such as SDR Sharp or SDR-radio.

"The most popular way to become operational is by using a transverter. Most transverters use a 144MHz or 432MHz intermediate frequency (IF). There are a number of commercial transverters available and designs have appeared in amateur radio publications over the years. Several of these have gone on to become kits. Popular 10GHz transverter kits are available from the same sources as for 1.2GHz, namely Kuhne Electronic (DB6NT) and Down East Microwave Incorporated (DEMI), as well as kits from GW4DGU. Ready built 10GHz transverters are also available from several of these manufacturers.

"The 10GHz band is not like VHF or even UHF, in that you may not get as many QSOs on the microwave bands as you would on the lower bands, but you don't take up microwaves to have large numbers of QSOs, you do it because you are interested in radio propagation, microwave technology and pushing the boundaries of amateur radio."

"So what can you expect to work on microwaves? In free space microwave signals do not suffer any greater loss than signals at lower frequencies, but the majority of radio signal paths have to contend with obstructions such as hills, the curvature of the earth and even buildings and trees. The signal loss caused by these obstructions is higher (often much higher) at microwaves than at HF and VHF, so it is this loss that limits the range of signals at 1.2GHz and above.

"Microwave signals can usually propagate to a distance about 1/3 farther than line of sight. This is due to refraction in the atmosphere, where signals are bent back towards the surface of the Earth as the air thins at increasing altitude. Refraction is constantly changing, so that the distance signals are refracted can vary from less than line of sight to distances of thousands of miles.

"Day-to-day propagation, at distances beyond line of sight, is mainly due to tropospheric scatter (troposcatter). Weak but useable signals can propagate to distances approaching 1,000km by scatter from small variations in the refractive index of the troposphere.

"Whilst there is no ionospheric-mode propagation at 10GHz, limited meteor scatter contacts have been made at 1.2GHz and amateur radio aurora propagation is theoretically possible on this band.

"Most microwave propagation takes place in the lower few km of the earth's atmosphere, unlike HF where propagation is mainly in the ionosphere. The lower atmosphere is where the weather is located and therefore the various weather phenomenon have a large influence of how well signals are propagated.

"Rain and snow scatter, extreme ducting, aircraft scatter, efficient obstacle reflections are all lots of paths that still need exploration and, if portable is your interest, who can beat being out on the hills in the right weather?

"In all then, the microwave bands offer enormous scope for home construction, ingenuity and experimentation."

Moonbounce or Earth-Moon-Earth (EME)

In some respects EME operation is about as far out as you can get in amateur radio. It involves bouncing your radio signals off the surface of the Moon and receiving them back on earth.

Just like microwaves, EME operation is not for outright beginners. It needs the right equipment, excellent antennas and a lot of power, although modern digital techniques have made it more accessible than ever before.

Many radio amateurs think that EME is a relatively new technique, but its origins go back quite a way. The Moon as a passive communications satellite was first proposed by British General Post Office (GPO) in 1940, when it was calculated it might be possible to beam microwave signals up from Earth and reflect them off the Moon.

Moonbounce was developed by the United States military in the years after World War II, with the first successful reception of echoes off the Moon being carried out on January 10, 1946. They used a 3 kilowatt transmitter.

The moon is a poor radio reflector, a quarter of a million miles away.

Getting Started in Amateur Radio

The project that followed led to more practical uses, including a teletype link between the naval base at Pearl Harbor, Hawaii and United States Navy headquarters in Washington, DC. The first amateur detection of signals from the Moon took place in 1953, between W4AO and W3GK on 2m (144MHz).

There are a lot of factors that need to be overcome for a successful EME contact. The first is that the Moon is around 250,000 miles away, so it is a round trip of about half a million miles. In fact, as the Moon is not in a circular orbit, this varies from around 252,711 miles (406,700km), to as 'little' as 221,456 miles (356,400km). This means that, at the speed of light, your signals take around 2.5 seconds to make the trip and back. You can actually hear your echoes off the Moon!

The next problem is that the Moon is not a very good reflector of radio waves – in fact it only reflects about 7%. This means that paths losses are enormous; around 250dB or more. You also get Doppler shift, as the Moon rises and sets, plus Faraday rotation – the rotation of the radio wave's polarisation as the electromagnetic wave interacts with the charged particles and the Earth's magnetic field. Plus you have libration fading to contend with. This is signal fading caused by the movement of the Moon and its surface imperfections. The higher the frequency, the faster the fading.

The Moon is also actually a very small target from Earth, being only around one degree wide. You also have to contend with cosmic and solar noise – at the time of a new Moon, when you would be beaming at the Sun as well as the Moon, it gets even harder due to solar noise.

If you are still interested in EME there are ways around these problems including (a) having a very efficient antenna system that can be accurately tracked, and (b) running quite a lot of power. This certainly isn't something for a 10W VHF radio and a colinear! You'll also need quality low-loss coax, such as Heliax.

Earlier EME attempts were made using CW (Morse) and speech (SSB), but more recently K1JT's JT modes with digital signal processing have made it a lot easier. You can read more about JT in the CW and digital modes chapter, but basically it allows the reception of EME signals that are below the noise level.

So what bands do people make EME contacts on and what sort of equipment do they use? Amateurs are using everything from 6m (50MHz) right up to the upper microwave bands. 6m isn't that popular, as the antenna system needed is huge. 2m (144MHz), 70cm (432MHz) and 23cm (1296MHz) are popular bands, where you can phase two or more Yagi beam antennas to get the required gain. The full legal limit (400W) is also useful, so that rules out Foundation and Intermediate licence holders.

It is possible to make JT-65 digital contacts off the moon on 2m using 100W and a single 16-element Yagi, but that should be regarded as an absolute minimum. The 50W power limit of the Intermediate licence could theoretically be used to make EME contacts on 2m, and certainly on 23cm, if you had an antenna array with enough gain.

If you want to use CW then you may need to move up to four stacked Yagis.

There isn't enough room here for a detailed technical look at EME, but let's finish with a quick case study from John Worsnop, G4BAO, who works EME from his back garden in Waterbeach, Cambridgeshire.

Back Garden GHz Bands EME at G4BAO

"I decided not to take the conventional first steps in to EME, namely a JT modes single Yagi

144MHz system, as I wanted to use bands above 1GHz and did not want to take up more than a corner of my patio.

"Microwave EME theory and practice are close and it should be 'satisfyingly predictable'. That said, there are no short cuts, you never stop tweaking your system and it takes time to make something work. For me it took two years from concept to first QSO. Which band you use is determined by your patio size, dish size, QRO amplifier availability and cost, so how did I decide?

"Software by VK3UM called EMECalc is a 'must have'. It automates system calculations and can be used for a 'what if' analysis of band, dish size and shape, feed type, power and receiver performance, enabling you to know if a system will work before you start collecting equipment.

G4BAO's EME dish in his back garden.

"Firstly, which band? For most people the starting point will be determined by what antenna can be accommodated. My first system used a 1.4m solid aluminium dish, which was small enough to pick up and carry and cost me nothing. This can be hidden with a garden furniture cover when not in use. For simplicity I decided on a polar mount for the dish. I was looking for a system that would work the 'big guns' on CW, would work JT modes and could give me detectable echoes.

"Based on calculations with EMECalc and the availability of cheap surplus solid state amplifiers I quickly settled on 2,320MHz, where a preamp noise figure of 0.35dB and a TX power of 100-200W is achievable and will get you QSOs.

"To keep feeder losses down, the transverter needed to be remote from the shack, so the whole unit was fitted in a watertight Storno base station cabinet. It was locked to a 10MHz reference and run on 28V DC, fed out from the house.

"The dish used a TVRO mount modified with declination adjustment using the latitude adjuster of a second dish mount. Manual setting of declination was done on each moon pass and was adequate for such a small dish.

"The single-axis drive for the dish was with a conventional satellite jackarm motor and an old Nokia ACU8152 positioner. I calibrated the positioner by plotting sun noise over a day.

"Setting the whole system up required optimisation of the dish and feed, based on measuring ratio of sun noise to 'cold sky' noise, finding the position of the feed that gives best sun/cold sky and adjusting the choke ring on the feed.

"The results of first two days operation over a contest weekend produced CW QSOs with, F2TU, OK1CA, ES5PC, G3LTF and a JT65c QSO with OK1DFC.

References:
1. VK3UM EMEcalc.   www.vk3um.com/eme%20calculator.htm
2. The Bodger's Guide to Patio Moonbounce. http://www.g4bao.com/Files/MRT2010.pdf
3. Optimising a *really* small EME system.
   http://www.g4bao.com/Files/G4BAO_MRT2013.pdf

Getting Started in Amateur Radio

Low Frequency (LF)

If you like the technical aspects of the hobby the low frequency bands may well appeal. These are the very long wavelength bands at the bottom of the spectrum available to radio amateurs, namely 136kHz (135.7-137.8kHz) or 2200 metres, and 472kHz (472-479kHz) or 600 metres. They are used for CW (Morse), QRSS (very slow Morse) and narrow-band digital modes.

The UK's lowest amateur band at 136kHz was introduced in 1998, following experiments at 73kHz. It is a challenging, but rewarding band. Although the power limit is just 1W effective radiated power (ERP), any practical antenna will be so small compared with the wavelength of operation, and therefore inefficient, that almost all operators radiate much less than this.

The 472kHz band can currently only be used by Full (Advanced) licensees, but there is nothing to stop others listening to the band and/or finding out more about it for when they upgrade their licences. This part of the radio spectrum – between the Long and Medium Wave broadcast bands – was used for many years for Morse communication between ships and the shore. It is also the top end of the aircraft non-directional beacon (NDB) band. Marine use was discontinued some time ago, but many aircraft NDBs are currently still active and those close to the 472kHz band can be used as beacons for optimising your receive set-up.

Following experimental use of 501-504kHz in the UK from 2007, and after years of lobbying by amateur radio societies, a world-wide allocation was obtained at 472kHz (472-479kHz) in January 2013, and the 500kHz experiments were closed down.

So what can you expect from these low bands? Firstly, you won't hear SSB signals, because these very small allocations are reserved entirely for narrowband modes such as CW, QRSS and datamodes, such as WSPR and Opera. Datamodes are the easiest way to monitor the activity.

QRSS is very slow Morse code, with a dot length of between 3 and 60 seconds. It is displayed on a PC using software that shows the dots and dashes of the

You can receive LF signals on a small loop, such as this Wellbrook ALA1530S, but you'll need something bigger for transmitting.

Morse characters on a computer screen. The very long dot length means you will be able to 'see' signal levels well below the levels at which they would be audible.

It also means it is easy to read, as there is plenty of time to look up the Morse characters. It is possible to receive stations from all over Europe on both bands, whilst well-equipped stations can receive signals from North America and beyond.

So what do you need to get started on LF? Well, to listen you can use just about any receiver capable of covering the band, although you may find a commercial transceiver a little insensitive unless you use a dedicated pre-amp.

Most important is the antenna. With wavelengths of 600m or longer, any effective transmitting antenna will be quite big, though an efficient receive-only antenna (eg a loop) can be made much smaller. A 'long-wire' antenna will work at LF, but it will need to be artificially lengthened by adding a tuner, usually comprising a loading coil.

There are very few commercial transmitters, so most people use home-made equipment. Transverters or transmitters are followed by power amplifiers, and there are several tried and tested designs available for both bands.

Anyone wanting to learn more about these bands should read *LF Today - A Guide to Success on the Bands Below 1MHz*, written by Mike Dennison, G3XDV, and available from the RSGB Shop. You might also benefit from joining the RSGB LF Group Yahoo! group, where you can find news, skeds, technical information and advice.

Echolink

Echolink is a system that lets radio amateurs communicate across the internet.

But why should I bother, I hear you say? If I wanted to do that I could use Skype or Google Hangouts. The difference with Echolink is that we can interface our radios with the system, thereby creating a hybrid radio/computer network. And Echolink is only available for use by radio amateurs.

The EchoLink software allows licensed radio amateurs to communicate with one another over the Internet, using streaming-audio technology. There are more than 200,000 validated Echolink users worldwide in 151 of the world's 193 nations, with about 5,200 online at any given time. Echolink was designed by Jonathan Taylor, K1RFD.

To use Echolink you must first install the software, which can be downloaded from www.echolink.org. There are versions available for Windows, Mac OSX and IOS, and Linux machines.

Before using the system the user's callsign must be validated. The EchoLink system requires that each new user provides positive proof of his or her licence and identity before their callsign is added to the list of validated users. This ensures that this system is used only by licensed amateur radio operators.

Once this is done there are effectively two modes. The first is single user mode. If you have an Internet-connected computer you can use the computer's microphone and speakers to connect to other EchoLink-enabled computers and talk to the amateur at the other end. The Echolink software will show you who is online. This can be a direct (one-to-one) connection or via an Echolink-equipped repeater or gateway. This means that you might be using an Internet connection, but the person you are talking to across the world could be using a 2m hand portable.

Some amateurs have also set up Echolink gateways that you can call into with your handheld.

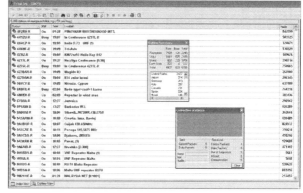

Echolink lets you have amateur radio 'QSOs' with other hams via your computer.

Getting Started in Amateur Radio

To connect from this to other gateways or Echolink users you usually have to use the DTMF tones on your transceiver to make the connection. It is best to ask the gateway or repeater owner for any instructions they may have.

It is also possible to connect your own VHF or UHF transceiver to your Internet-connected PC with a specially-designed hardware interface. Doing this enables another radio amateur with their own transceiver, who is within radio range of this station, to communicate with (or through) any other EchoLink-equipped station anywhere in the world. This is quite advanced and it is probably best left alone unless you are really keen and have a comprehensive knowledge of how Echolink works.

EchoLink software is also available for the Apple iPhone, iPad, and iPod Touch via the Apple App Store. An edition of EchoLink has also been released for the Android platform and is available in the Google Play Store.

When you first install Echolink you may find that, whatever you do, you can't hear anything. This is because your router might be blocking the Echolink connection. EchoLink requires that your router or firewall allows inbound and outbound UDP to ports 5198 and 5199, and outbound TCP to port 5200. If you are using a home network router you will also need to configure the router to 'forward' UDP ports 5198 and 5199 to the PC on which EchoLink is running. If you go to Echolink.org it will explain how you can unblock those ports on your router, which should then mean you can make and receive Echolink connections.

Echolink might not seem like real radio, especially as you will be using your computer, but it can be used to contact like-minded radio amateurs with a fairly flawless connection. It also lets you connect to repeaters or 'nodes' all over the world. As such it is a useful tool for radio amateurs to have, especially if you can't erect a very good HF antenna.

The future

As I said at the beginning of the book there are so many facets to amateur radio that you should never be bored! From SSTV to PSK31, from SSB to CW, and from DXing to special event stations, there really is something for everybody.

And all you need is a licence and a radio – and you can get the former in just a couple of weekends.

I hope this book has encouraged you to find out more about what this fantastic hobby has to offer.